MENSA®
® THE HIGH IQ SOCIETY

Holiday Puzzles 1

THIS IS A CARLTON BOOK

Text and puzzle content © British Mensa Limited 1995, 1996, 1998.
Design and artwork © Carlton Books Limited 1995, 1996, 1998.

A CIP catalogue record for this book is available from the British Library.

ISBN 978-1-84732-349-1

Text and puzzles in this edition first appeared in:
Mensa Mind Mazes for Kids
Mensa Lateral Thinking and Logical Deduction
Mensa New Number Puzzles
Mensa Mighty Mindbusters
Mensa Family Quiz Book

Printed and bound in the UK by CPI Mackays, Chatham ME5 8TD

MENSA®
THE HIGH IQ SOCIETY

Holiday Puzzles 1

Puzzles, Quizzes and Mind Mazes –
mental stimulation to enjoy on vacation

Robert Allen • John Bremner • Dave Chatten • Carolyn Skitt

CARLTON
BOOKS

What is Mensa?

Mensa is the international society for people with a high IQ.
We have more than 100,000 members in over 40 countries worldwide.

The society's aims are:
   to identify and foster human intelligence for the benefit of humanity
   to encourage research in the nature, characteristics, and uses of intelligence
   to provide a stimulating intellectual and social environment for its members

Anyone with an IQ score in the top two per cent of population is eligible to
become a member of Mensa – are you the 'one in 50' we've been looking for?

Mensa membership offers an excellent range of benefits:
   Networking and social activities nationally and around the world
   Special Interest Groups – hundreds of chances to pursue your hobbies
      and interests – from art to zoology!
   Monthly members' magazine and regional newsletters
   Local meetings – from games challenges to food and drink
   National and international weekend gatherings and conferences
   Intellectually stimulating lectures and seminars
   Access to the worldwide SIGHT network for travellers and hosts

For more information about Mensa: www.mensa.org, or

British Mensa Ltd.,
St John's House,
St John's Square,
Wolverhampton
WV2 4AH
Telephone: +44 (0) 1902 772771
E-mail: enquiries@mensa.org.uk
www.mensa.org.uk

Contents

Welcome, puzzle-lover!

The puzzles in this book are presented in sections, but you don't have to work your way through the book from start to finish. If you feel like doing the quizzes first, or all of the number puzzles in one go, feel free – the order is up to you. There's only one exception – the Mind Maze should be completed in one go, because the answers all add up to a big, final solution.

Good luck, and happy puzzling!

How do you solve a Mind Maze? In each maze the puzzles are linked in a certain order which is quite different from their numerical order in the book. The answer to each puzzle is constructed in such a way that it guides you to the next one in the series. For example, let's take a puzzle like this:

Find the number in this series. When you have the answer, double it and go to the next puzzle.

2   4   6   8   10   ?

The series increases by two at each step, so the number to replace the question mark is 12. You then double it to make 24 and that is the number of the next puzzle you should attempt.

Quite often in these mazes we use letters instead of numbers. To help you we have used only one system for conversion: a simple substitution based on alphabetical position, so that, for example, A = 1, B = 2, ... M = 13, N = 14, ... Z = 26.

Now off you go...

The Daily Globe has obtained tickets for a concert to be given by Tocsin, a new band that is just so amazingly cool you would give an arm and both legs to be there. Happily no major surgery is called for. The first person to solve the maze and send in their answer to the *Globe*'s editor gets to see the show and meet Tocsin live!

TOCSIN TIME

Find the next letter in the series. If you choose T, go to 15.
If you choose L, go to 23. If you choose D, go to 12. If you
choose M, go to 11.

A →4 **E** ←2 **C** →4 **G** ←2 **E**

→4 **I** ←2 **G** **K** 4 **I** ←2 **?**

M

(11)

TOCSIN TIME

There is a pop group hidden in the grid.
Hint: Water music! When you have found
them, go to the puzzle which is the first
letter's position in the alphabet.

W	E	E
E	T	W
W	T	T

A strange signboard! It has nothing to do with geography. If we tell you that the vowels and consonants have different values, can you work out how far it is to Caen? Add 7 to your answer and go to the next question.

? CAEN

18.

PARIS 24

?X $\frac{3}{6}$ + 32 6

30 ST. MALO

DIEPPE 27

ca 6, V 3.

Since 100 AD, has a new century e.g. 200, 1000, 1900 and so on, ever started on a Sunday? If you answer yes, go to 30. If you answer no, go to 19.

MIND MAZE

This grid contains the name of a famous river, plus one extra letter. What letter is left over after you have found the name? If you choose D, go to 20. If you choose S, go to 31. If you choose P, go to 17.

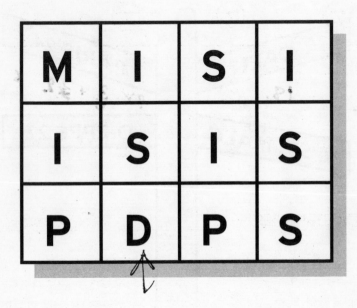

If five equals 4, six equals 3 and sixteen equals 7, what does twenty-six equal? Hint: This isn't a magic spell. Add 18 to your answer and go to the next question.

MIND MAZE

Which is the odd one out in this series? If you choose A, go to 30. If you choose B, go to 27. If you choose C, go to 13. If you choose D, go to 22.

A **B** **C** **D**

Each circle works according to the same strange logic. When you have cracked it you should be able to complete the final circle with a number. Add 14 to your answer and go to the next problem.

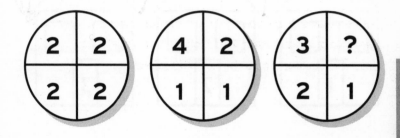

The boxes represent the gas, water and electricity services. You have to connect each service by a line drawn to each house. The lines must never cross each other, nor must they cross one of the boxes or one of the houses. How many ways of doing this are there? If you find more than 3 ways, go to 17. If you find only two ways, go to 29. If you find one way, go to 26. If you can't do it, go to 3.

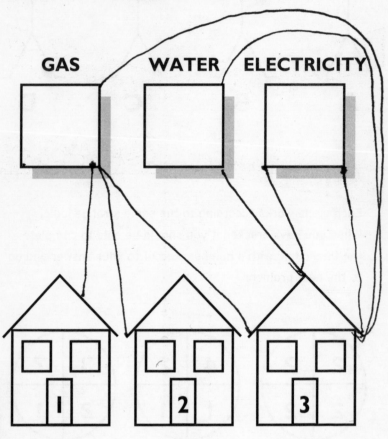

This signpost has nothing to do with real distances, but is based on the value of vowels and consonants. How far is Cambridge? Subtract 33 from your answer and go to the next puzzle.

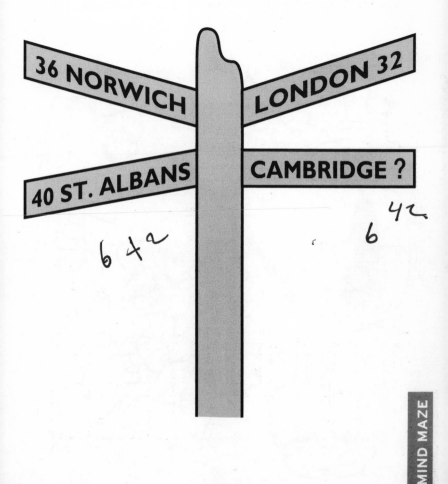

Scrooge was no fool. He saved the ends of candles, melted them down and made new candles out of them. If 4 ends would make a new candle, how many more candles would he get in total when he had burned 48 new ones. Beware! This is not as easy as it looks. Your first answer is partly correct but you must think one stage further. When you have the answer add 9 and go to the next puzzle.

There is an American President hidden in this grid. When you find his name you will see that we have added one extra letter. What is it? Convert your answer to a number based on its position in the alphabet. Halve it and go to that location.

B	C	I	I
L	L	L	L
N	N	O	T

Find the odd one out. If you think it is spider, go to 17. If you think it is mantis, go to 23. If you think it is ant, go to 3. If you think it is cricket, go to 29.

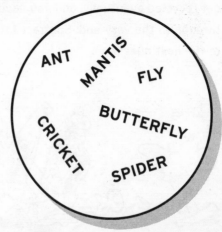

ANT MANTIS FLY BUTTERFLY CRICKET SPIDER

Find the odd one out. Subtract 24 from your answer and go
to the next puzzle.

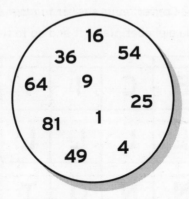

A bottle factory melts down broken old bottles to make new
ones. If they start with the remains of 279 bottles, and they
can get one new one out of three old ones, how many new
bottles can be made in total? Beware! Even the new ones
get recycled eventually, and you have to think this one right
through to the very end. Subtract 131 from your total and go
to the next puzzle.

MIND MAZE

Three geographical locations are hidden in this grid. Which is the odd one out? Convert the first letter of the odd one out into a number based on its position in the alphabet, add 12 and go to the next puzzle.

I	E	Y	E	A
U	S	T	I	P
A	R	L	O	A

What is the next number in this series? Subtract 43 and go to the next puzzle.

2   4   7   14   17

34   37   ?

TOCSIN TIME

PUZZLE 18

Which is the odd one out? If you choose cod, go to 12. If you choose herring, go to 22. If you choose whale, go to 26.

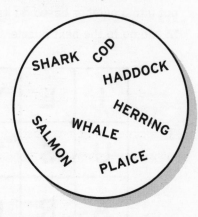

SHARK COD HADDOCK HERRING WHALE SALMON PLAICE

TOCSIN TIME

PUZZLE 19

Find the odd number out (which is actually a sort of hint). If you choose 102, go to 14. If you choose 131, go to 29. If you choose 72, go to 27.

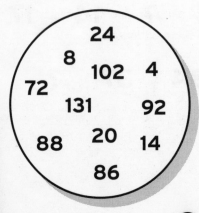

24 8 102 4 72 131 92 88 20 14 86

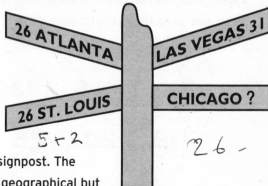

26 ATLANTA

LAS VEGAS 31

26 ST. LOUIS

CHICAGO ?

5 + 2

26 -

This is a strange signpost. The distances are not geographical but are based on the values of vowels and consonants. Can you work out the distance to Chicago? When you have the answer subtract 19 and go to the next question.

Scrooge has a thrifty habit of saving soap. From the remains of three bars he can make one new one. How many bars can he make, in total, from the remains of nine new ones? Add 14 to your answer and go to the next location.

MIND MAZE

What number would continue the series? Divide your answer in half and go to the next puzzle.

2   7   8   13   14

19   20   25   ?

Which is the odd one out? If you choose sun, go to 10. If you choose hurricane, go to 27. If you choose storm, go to 17.

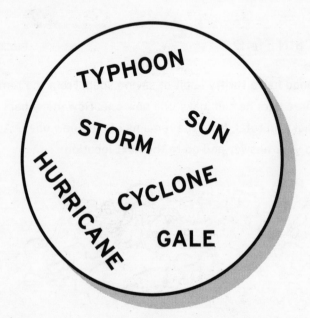

According to the logic of this puzzle, would the number 10 go above or below the line. If you choose above, go to 4. If you choose below, go to 10. Hint: The actual figures won't help you.

$$\frac{1 \quad 3 \quad 5 \quad 7 \quad 8 \quad 9}{2 \quad\quad 4 \quad\quad 6} \quad ?$$

What number continues the series? Add 3 to your answer and go to the next puzzle.

1   4   8   11   15   18   22   ?

MIND MAZE

Which number is the odd one out?
Subtract 14 from your answer and go
to the next question.

Which letter continues the series? Convert your letter into a
number based on its position in the alphabet. Then subtract
3 and go to the next puzzle.

MIND MAZE

T T T F F
S S E N ?

Old Scrooge recycles blunt and used wax crayons. From 10 old pencils he can make a brand new one. How many can he produce in total if he starts off with 200 crayons? Be warned, you must follow the logic right through to the end. When you have the answer, subtract 8 and go to the next puzzle.

MIND MAZE

How many squares of any size can you see in the grid? When you have the answer subtract 12 and go to the next puzzle.

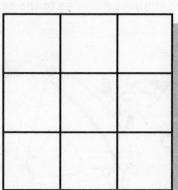

Should the number 10 go above or below the line? If you choose above, go to 12. If you choose below, go to 10.

1 2   6

3 4 5   7 8 9   **?**

MIND MAZE

Congratulations! This is the end of the Mind Maze. Will you get to see Tocsin? Add together all the locations you visited on your journey between 26 and 27 (inclusive) to get your final answer.

In the Dirt

Two children were playing in the loft of a barn before it gave way and they fell to the ground below. When they dusted themselves off, the face of one was dirty while the other's was clean. Only the clean-faced boy went off to wash his face. Why?

Clues

1. Neither of them needed cold water to stop bruising and neither child was hurt.
2. Neither child put their dirty hands on their faces.
3. It was dusty and they had both sweated.
4. Their faces had not touched the ground.

See answer page 200

The Holiday Disaster

Bill Drallam and his lifelong companion did not like the cold
weather and often flew south for a winter break. This year they
decided that they would go with other friends in a larger group.
They reached the airport and most of the group were killed,
together with 30 people they had
never met before. The
survivors who suffered
injury who were in
their group were not
taken to hospital,
yet all of the other
survivors with injuries
were. Can you explain
what occurred?

Clues

1. Members from their group caused the problem.
2. They did not cause the problem deliberately.
3. No disease or virus was involved.
4. It was not a terrorist or hijack situation.
5. It had nothing to do with guns.
6. If they had not gone with the larger group the 30
   strangers may have survived.

See answer page 200

Evolution

Three uninhabited islands were within swimming distance from each other but only at certain times of the year. This depended on the strong currents that flowed between them. A group of naturalist explorers put animal x on island A, animal y on island B and animal z on island C. No other animals were on the islands and no animals visited the islands.

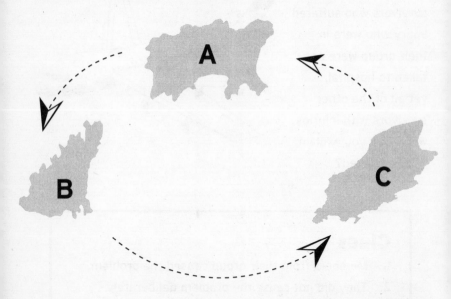

When the explorers returned several years later they found island A had no animals on it. Island B had animals x and y plus one new animal on it, and island C had the same type of animals as island B plus z and another new animal. Can you name the five animals?

See answer page 200

The Full Cask of Wine

Following a shipwreck a case of wine is washed ashore and is
lodged precariously on some rocks on the seashore. The sole
inhabitant of the island only has a bottle with a rubber seal which
fits the bunghole at the top of the cask exactly. He also has
an endless supply of fresh drinking water. He cannot move the
barrel at all and cannot break the cask for fear of losing all of the
contents. How does he get the wine into the bottle if he is not
allowed to put water into the cask and he does not wish to spoil
the wine?

**Hole at the top
of the cask**

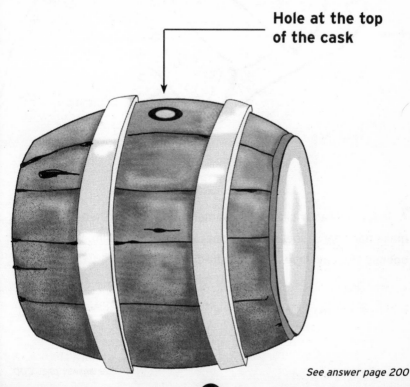

See answer page 200

Recovering with a Letter

A deaf lady was tricked by a conman who told her that he could make her hear if she bought a special letter from him. When she opened the envelope what did she find?

See answer page 200

The Twins Cause Confusion

A father always wanted 4 sons. His ancestors had always had large families and so he gave it little thought. He was, however, upset in later life because he had only produced 3 sons. His eldest son was now 28 years old and he had given him a quarter of his land as his inheritance already. He had not passed other shares to his other sons before a wonderful event occurred: twins, and both boys! He immediately split the remaining land into four identically-shaped parts, which were also equal in area, and gave each remaining child a share. How did he do this, given that he had divided the land awkwardly?

1st Son's Land

See answer page 200

How to Trick the Genie?

The king had a magic lamp which contained a genie. He also had a beautiful daughter who loved Aladdin, but the king did not like Aladdin and did not wish them to marry. He did not wish to upset his daughter, so one day he rubbed the lamp and devised a plan with the genie. The king said he would call upon Aladdin and his daughter and seek a test of worthiness from the genie for Aladdin. They would all have to abide by the results. Aladdin was passing by when he heard the king and the genie planning the event. The genie said, "I will produce two envelopes for Aladdin to choose his fate. We will tell him that one contains the words 'Get Married' and the other will contain the words 'Banished Forever.' Aladdin must choose one envelope, but I will make sure that both envelopes have 'Banished Forever.'"

How did Aladdin trick the genie and the king?

See answer page 200

36

Car Grid

You are in a car that is parked and facing east on a straight road. You set off in the direction of the facing road and after some time driving you finish up 2.7 miles to the west of where you started.

How?

Clues

1. It is not a car with hovering capabilities.
2. It is not on a trailer or being towed.
3. You have not gone around the world.
4. You cannot turn the car around.

See answer page 200

The Earth

01 What is the name given to the Earth's hard outer shell?

02 Which science studies the history, structure, and composition of the Earth?

03 Images of ancient living creatures are sometimes found trapped in rock. What are these called?

04 What is the study of the Earth's surface called?

05 Is the Earth a perfect sphere?

06 What do we call the metallic centre of the Earth?

07 How much of the Earth's surface is covered by water?

08 What is the name of the continent which contains the South Pole?

09 What do we call a gap in the Earth's crust through which molten rock escapes onto the Earth's surface?

10 What do we call a shallow depression at the top of a volcanic cone?

11 What is a geyser?

12 What name is given to the sudden emergence of hot material from the Earth's interior?

13 What does the Richter scale measure?

14 What name is sometimes given to the tidal wave set off by an undersea earthquake?

15 What do we call a hill over 2,000 ft (600 m) high?

16 What do we call the imaginary lines that divide the Earth from north to south?

17 What do we call the imaginary lines that divide the Earth from east to west?

18 What is the process by which rock is worn down by weather?

19 What is the name given to the heaps of rock debris formed by frost shattering?

20 Does a stalagmite grow up or down?

21 What is the name for a place where a stream disappears underground in limestone scenery?

22 What is glaciation?

23 What is a glacier?

24 What is an ice age?

25 What is the Norwegian word for a long, deep sea inlet gouged out by a glacier?

26 What is a moraine?

27 What is permafrost?

28 What is a peninsula?

29 What do we call a band of sand, shingle, or pebbles at the edge of the sea?

30 What is strange about the Mediterranean Sea?

31 What is the name for an underwater ridge created by the coral polyp?

32 What is the name for an area of land surrounded by water?

33 What do we call the twice daily rise and fall of the oceans?

34 What is a spring tide?

35 What do we call the thin layer of gases surrounding the Earth?

36 What is the commonest gas in the atmosphere?

37 What is the greenhouse effect?

38 What is a barometer?

39 What is a thermometer?

40 What do we call a stream of air moving from one place to another?

41 Complete the following sentence: An isobar is a line on a map that links points of equal atmospheric...

42 What do we call a dense cloud of water droplets close to the ground?

43 What is humidity?

44 The Beaufort scale describes the effects of various wind speeds. What is the highest speed called?

45 According to the Beaufort scale, is a storm stronger than a gale?

46 What is oil?

47 What is coal?

48 What is so-called 'natural gas' mainly made of?

49 What colour are emeralds?

50 What are the three rare metals most used in jewellery?

Answers to this quiz are on page 201

Pot Luck

01 Is there more or less water now than when the seas were first formed?

02 Spider, horseshoe, and hermit are all varieties of which sea creature?

03 Which of the following is not a sign of the zodiac? (a) Libra, (b) Aquarius, (c) Ceres, (d) Capricorn

04 What name is given to a white animal with pink eyes (eg, mouse or rabbit)?

05 What sort of game is Yahtzee?

06 Which of the following is not usually a gambling game? (a) poker, (b) roulette, (c) dice (craps), (d) patience

07 The leaves of which water plant are called pads?

08 John Constable was:
(a) a doctor, (b) a painter, (c) an explorer,
(d) a president of the USA

09 Carmen is:
(a) an opera, (b) a car, (c) a game of chance

10 Which large aircraft has a name that reminds you of an elephant?

11 Which of the following is not a make of car?
(a) Rolls Royce, (b) Boeing, (c) Chevrolet,
(d) Peugeot

12 Would a ship called a brigantine be equipped with sails or an engine?

13 Who was the King of Rock 'n' Roll?
(a) Cliff Richard, (b) Mick Jagger, (c) Elvis Presley,
(d) Paul McCartney

14 In the northern hemisphere, which wind would you expect to be colder – the north or the south?

15 Which is further north, Turkey or Switzerland?

16 Which city is smaller, São Paulo or Washington DC?

17 In which country would you not drive on the left?
(a) Thailand, (b) UK, (c) Sweden

18 What game do the Chicago Bulls play?

19 What do children have in common with young goats?

20 What are young swans called?

21 What are young geese called?

22 What is Esperanto?

23 By what other name is the Religious Society of Friends sometimes known?

24 Which animals are thought to commit mass suicide by hurling themselves into the sea?

25 Which of the following is not a citrus fruit?
(a) lemon, (b) rhubarb, (c) orange, (d) grapefruit

26 Bats' wings are really modified hands. True or false?

27 Is a Portugese Man o' War:
(a) a ship, (b) a warrior, (c) a jellyfish, (d) a car?

28 In which country was golf invented?
(a) USA, (b) Zaire, (c) Denmark, (d) Scotland

29 What sort of creature is a Bombay duck?

30 Where would you find the Everglades?

31 By what name did Westerners formerly know Beijing?

32 In which of these places is Chinese not the native
language? (a) Taiwan, (b) Hong Kong, (c) Korea

33 Which religious leader lives in the Vatican?

34 Where in a house would you expect to find the eaves?

35 What is a ravine?

36 Why can't you see around corners?

37 If you flip a coin, what are the chances of it coming down
heads?

38 In which country would you find the Sinai Desert?

39 How many years is three score and ten?

40 What is Blue John?

41 What causes hay fever?

42 Which country sent rhubarb to the West?

43 According to the Bible, what was used to feed the five thousand?

44 Which country is the home of the classical guitar?

45 What sort of creature could be described as a Thoroughbred, a Shetland, an Arab, or a Mustang?

46 What name is given to ancient Egyptian writing?

47 What is azure?

48 What is serendipity?

49 What is the difference between astrology and astronomy?

50 What other name is given to the constellation of Ursa Major?

Answers to this quiz are on pages 201-202

Synonyms

01 Alive is the same as:
(a) animated, (b) busy, (c) exciting.

02 Bleak is the same as: (a) cold, (b) gloomy, (c) hard.

03 Create is the same as: (a) make, (b) excite, (c) grow.

04 Drudge is the same as: (a) dull, (b) toil, (c) brown.

05 Eager is the same as:
(a) keen, (b) excited, (c) quick.

06 Fraternal is the same as:
(a) kindly, (b) wise, (c) brotherly.

07 Grotesque is the same as:
(a) funny, (b) bizarre, (c) obvious.

08 Liberal is the same as:
(a) free, (b) generous, (c) socialist.

09 Keepsake is the same as:
(a) memento, (b) gift, (c) bribe.

10 Ideal is the same as:
(a) cheap, (b) flawless, (c) useful.

11 Jocular is the same as:
(a) witty, (b) silly, (c) helpful.

12 Lucid is the same as:
(a) clean, (b) understandable, (c) tall.

13 Arcane is the same as:
(a) geometrical, (b) mysterious, (c) pretty.

14 Murky is the same as:
(a) dark, (b) dangerous, (c) insane.

15 Nimble is the same as:
(a) handy, (b) bright, (c) clever.

16 Oral is the same as: (a) verbal, (b) spoken, (c) loud.

17 Plural is the same as:
(a) several, (b) deceptive, (c) generous.

18 Robust is the same as: (a) red, (b) rough, (c) strong.

19 Refined is the same as:
(a) delicate, (b) snobbish, (c) precious.

20 Satisfied is the same as:
(a) pleased, (b) contented, (c) proud.

21 Trapped is the same as:
(a) killed, (b) caught, (c) closed.

22 Unlikely is the same as:
(a) unfortunate, (b) improbable, (c) difficult.

23 Valour is the same as:
(a) bravery, (b) virtue, (c) sincerity.

24 Want is the same as:
(a) have, (b) require, (c) hunger.

25 Alter is the same as:

(a) change, (b) enlarge, (c) sustain.

26 Break is the same as: (a) stop, (b) crack, (c) reform.

27 Caress is the same as: (a) whisper, (b) sing, (c) stroke.

28 Demand is the same as:

(a) ask, (b) leave, (c) endanger.

29 Element is the same as: (a) ring, (b) delete, (c) part.

30 Manufacture is the same as:

(a) industry, (b) make, (c) business.

31 Noble is the same as:

(a) wealthy, (b) honourable, (c) charitable.

32 Organize is the same as:

(a) arrange, (b) support, (c) lead.

33 Perpetual is the same as:

(a) infinite, (b) occasional, (c) continual.

34 Quantity is the same as:

(a) amount, (b) some, (c) enough.

35 Research is the same as:

(a) prosecute, (b) colleague, (c) inquiry.

36 Sample is the same as:

(a) specimen, (b) determine, (c) contents.

37 Treachery is the same as:

(a) cowardice, (b) disloyalty, (c) avarice.

38 Ungrateful is the same as:
(a) offensive, (b) bragging, (c) thankless.

39 Whip is the same as: (a) beat, (b) swipe, (c) deflate.

40 Yearn is the same as: (a) vomit, (b) crave, (c) delay.

41 Absolute is the same as:
(a) perfect, (b) summit, (c) greatness.

42 Brutish is the same as:
(a) dirty, (b) beastly, (c) concerned.

43 Concentrate is the same as:
(a) condense, (b) testify, (c) gratify.

44 Dangle is the same as:
(a) decorate, (b) hang, (c) destroy.

45 Earn is the same as: (a) behave, (b) acquire, (c) take.

46 Frequent is the same as:
(a) sometimes, (b) constantly, (c) often.

47 Grapple is the same as:
(a) handle, (b) wrestle, (c) frame.

48 Harken is the same as:
(a) listen, (b) wait, (c) entertain.

49 Begrudge is the same as: (a) envy, (b) dislike, (c) greed.

50 Leave is the same as: (a) depart, (b) escape,
(c) engross.

Answers to this quiz are on page 202

Nature

01 What is the difference between a moth and a butterfly?

02 What is the difference between a frog and a toad?

03 To what family do lions, tigers, and cheetahs belong?

04 What domestic animal is the closest relative of the wolf?

05 Where are penguins found?

06 Where are polar bears found?

07 Which common vegetable did Sir Walter Raleigh introduce to Europe?

08 Which birds are collectively known as a 'murder'?

09 What is the largest species of shark?

10 What is taxonomy?

11 What is the difference between frog spawn and toad spawn?

12 Which bird is notorious for laying its eggs in another bird's nest?

13 What is a dingo?

14 What is a feral animal?

15 What is the name for the Australian bird rather like an ostrich?

16 What domestic animal did the Egyptians worship as a god?

17 Do birds sing for pleasure?

18 Does a fish normally have lungs?

19 Is the cheetah the world's fastest running animal?

20 Is a sponge a plant?

21 Is a lizard warm- or cold- blooded?

22 Is it true that some birds can use tools?

23 To what family do spiders and scorpions belong?

24 To what family do crabs and lobsters belong?

25 What is the purpose of a rattlesnake's rattle?

26 Do male or female lions do the hunting?

27 What sort of creature is a koi?

28 Which blackbird is not black?

29 Which two animals were responsible for the spread of the Black Death?

30 Is a tomato a fruit or a vegetable?

31 In northern latitudes what are swallows famous for doing in autumn?

32 Is it true that the sight of seagulls inland means there are storms at sea?

33 Is the owl really wise?

34 Which animal defends itself by spraying enemies with an evil-smelling fluid?

35 Which creature is known as a glutton?

36 What do satsumas, clementines, and mandarins have in common?

37 What is another name for a Daddy Longlegs?

38 From which flower is opium produced?

39 What is lichen?

40 Which scavenging animal is famous for its laugh?

41 Where would you find alligators?

42 Are giant pandas herbivores?

43 What is a young swan called?

44 What is a young eel called?

45 What is another name for a dung beetle?

46 Does a frog have ears?

47 Oxeye is a variety of which common wild flower?

48 Girls called Erica are named after which wild flower?

49 What sort of creature is a stickleback?

50 What is the common name for fishes of the family Diodontidae, which have strong, sharp spines on the body and are capable of inflating themselves when attacked?

Answers to this quiz are on pages 202-203

The Human Body

01 What name is more usually given to the epidermis?

02 What do we call the collection of bones that supports the body?

03 What part of your body has auricles and ventricles?

04 What is a more common name for the patella?

05 Your hair and nails continue to grow after you are dead. True or false?

06 What part of the mouth is affected by periodontitis?

07 How many milk (first) teeth do we have?

08 What are the bones of the spine called?

09 In which body organ would you find a retina?

10 The body has two intestines; what are they called?

11 Men have a lump clearly visible at the front of the throat. What is the common name for it?

12 Is it true that men and women have different numbers of ribs?

13 What is the common name for the oesophagus?

14 What is the hard substance just under the white enamel of your teeth?

15 What is the average pulse rate for an adult at rest?

16 We have much more liver than we actually need. True or false?

17 Which human organ, shaped rather like a small sack, can become full of stones?

18 What is the technical name for the vertical bone that runs down the middle of the chest?

19 Where would you find the ulna and radius?

20 What is the technical name for the liquid waste which is collected in the bladder?

21 The skin is covered with millions of tiny holes. What are these called?

22 What effect does the diasease hemophilia have on the blood?

23 What is the name given to the large chewing teeth at the back of the mouth?

24 What is the pigment that gives some people brown skin?

25 Where in the body would you find saliva?

26 What is dandruff?

27 What is the disease in which the body's joints wear out?

28 Which are the smallest blood vessels:
(a) arteries, (b) capillaries or (c) veins?

29 What is myopia?

30 Where would you find the tibia and fibula?

31 What is the name for the two spongey organs with which we breathe?

32 Which of these is not a body organ:
(a) eulogy, (b) spleen, or (c) pancreas?

33 Which organs transmit messages from parts of the body to the brain?

34 By what other name are the front cutting teeth known?

35 In what part of the body would you find a drum?

36 What is the mat of muscle that makes the lungs move?

37 What is inside the eyeball?

38 In which organ of the body would you find the pituitary gland?

39 What is the bone to which the legs are attached?

40 What is the main purpose of sweating?

41 In which part of the body would you find biceps and triceps?

42 Which part of the body is attacked by the disease meningitis?

43 Which childhood disease causes the salivary glands in the jaw to swell dramatically?

44 Which of these is not part of the body: (a) coccyx, (b) occiput, or (c) pachyderm?

45 What is the process called, by which food is broken down and nutrition extracted?

46 What is the technical name for breathing?

47 Where would you find the gluteus maximus muscles?

48 Which part of the inner ear controls our sense of balance?

49 What is the condition in which a small part of the stomach lining is attacked and inflamed by gastric juices?

50 Which substance, associated with animal fat, is responsible for the narrowing of arteries?

Answers to this quiz are on pages 203-204

Opposites

01 The opposite of eager is: (a) slovenly, (b) lethargic, (c) disinterested.

02 The opposite of grateful is: (a) thankless, (b) euphoric, (c) ingratiating.

03 The opposite of generous is: (a) mean, (b) rich, (c) spiteful.

04 The opposite of captive is: (a) escape, (b) free, (c) release.

05 The opposite of profound is: (a) abysmal, (b) superficial, (c) recondite.

06 The opposite of lazy is: (a) busy, (b) keen, (c) industrious.

07 The opposite of real is: (a) imaginary, (b) dream, (c) strange.

08 The opposite of tense is (a) happy, (b) relaxed, (c) sleepy.

09 The opposite of defunct is: (a) extant, (b) extinct, (c) bygone.

10 The opposite of increase is: (a) poverty, (b) less, (c) decrease.

11 The opposite of frivolous is: (a) flighty, (b) jejune, (c) earnest.

12 The opposite of total is: (a) some, (b) most, (c) partial.

13 The opposite of grief is: (a) parsimony,
(b) delectation, (c) rectitude.

14 The opposite of crowded is: (a) replete, (b) vacuous,
(c) sordid.

15 The opposite of jejune is: (a) mediocre, (b) insipid,
(c) fascinating.

16 The opposite of gravid is: (a) barren, (b) light,
(c) hilarious.

17 The opposite of sell is: (a) invest, (b) purchase, (c) haggle.

18 The opposite of energetic is: (a) drowsy, (b) listless,
(c) asleep.

19 The opposite of retreat is: (a) flee, (b) advance, (c) fight.

20 The opposite of sharp is: (a) dull, (b) cloudy, (c) witty.

21 The opposite of quiescent is: (a) frolicsome, (b) noisy,
(c) gradual?

22 The opposite of glum is: (a) morose, (b) laughter,
(c) cheerful.

23 The opposite of conflate is: (a) deflate, (b) overlook,
(c) disperse.

24 The opposite of stupid is: (a) learned, (b) clever,
(c) knowledgeable.

25 The opposite of degrade is: (a) promote, (b) grow, (c) fertilize.

26 The opposite of sweet is: (a) acid, (b) piquant, (c) sour.

27 The opposite of catch is: (a) escape, (b) free, (c) deport.

28 The opposite of climb is: (a) fall, (b) abseil, (c) descend.

29 The opposite of barbarous is: (a) kind, (b) civilized, (c) polite.

30 The opposite of contempt: (a) esteem, (b) perdition, (c) contumely.

31 The opposite of preserve is: (a) encapsulate, (b) discreate, (c) render.

32 The opposite of optimistic is: (a) worried, (b) pessimistic, (c) unhappy.

33 The opposite of proponent is: (a) ally, (b) antagonist, (c) advocate.

34 The opposite of euphony is: (a) dissonance, (b) symphony, (c) criticism.

35 The opposite of create is: (a) establish, (b) dismantle, (c) reduce.

36 The opposite of satiety is: (a) glut, (b) starve, (c) dearth.

37 The opposite of intrinsic is: (a) extraneous, (b) excluded, (c) inculcated.

38 The opposite of hostile is: (a) surrender, (b) friendly, (c) malicious.

39 The opposite of tactful is: (a) blunt, (b) lying, (c) rude.

40 The opposite of gregarious is: (a) lonely, (b) withdrawn, (c) solitary.

41 The opposite of grow is: (a) decay, (b) shrink, (c) fall.

42 The opposite of convenient is: (a) handy, (b) awkward, (c) distant.

43 The opposite of flammable is: (a) inflammable, (b) combustible, (c) flameproof.

44 The opposite of diminutive is: (a) big, (b) global, (c) prolific.

45 The opposite of minuscule is: (a) microscopic, (b) huge, (c) enlarged.

46 The opposite of chaos is: (a) order, (b) conformity, (c) universe.

47 The opposite of arid is: (a) fertile, (b) wet, (c) marshy.

48 The opposite of hungry is: (a) greedy, (b) sick, (c) fed.

49 The opposite of bizarre is: (a) outlandish, (b) traditional, (c) grotesque.

50 The opposite of tasty is: (a) bland, (b) spicy, (c) disgusting.

Answers to this quiz are on page 204

Events

01 In which year did Kenya gain independence from Britain?
(a) 1922, (b) 1963, (c) 1973

02 In which year did Britain impose direct rule over Northern Ireland, and Ceylon change its name to Sri Lanka?

03 In which year was the state of Israel founded? (a) 1918, (b) 1945, (c) 1948

04 In which year did Eisenhower become president? (a) 1945, (b) 1952, (c) 1955

05 In which year did Valentina Tereshkova become the first woman in space?

06 In which year did the airship Hindenburg burst into flames and explode? (a) 1914, (b) 1932, (c) 1937

07 In which year did Adolf Hitler survive an assassination attempt?

08 Which year saw San Francisco's worst earthquake?
(a) 1888, (b) 1900, (c) 1906

09 In which year was the Wall Street Crash?

10 In which year did Robert Mugabe become the first black leader in Zimbabwe after independence? (a) 1980, (b) 1982, (c) 1983

11 In which year was the Ford Motor Company founded?
(a) 1872, (b) 1898, (c) 1903?

12 In which year was Mount Everest conquered for the first time?

13 In which year did the Falklands War take place? (a) 1982, (b) 1988, (c) 1991

14 In which year did the Live Aid concert take place? (a) 1980, (b) 1985, (c) 1989

15 In which year was George Orwell's novel *1984* published? (a) 1902, (b) 1933, (c) 1949

16 In which year did the spacecraft Apollo 16 land on the moon?

17 In which year did the Beatles score their first US number one hit? (a) 1960, (b) 1962, (c) 1964

18 In which year did the Suez Canal first open to traffic? (a) 1848, (b) 1869, (c) 1937

19 In which year did Brazil win soccer's World Cup, Salvador Allende become president of Chile, and Jimi Hendrix die of a drug overdose?

20 In which year did the Boxer Rising take place? (a) 1900, (b) 1918, (c) 1944

21 In which year did George Gershwin write *Rhapsody in Blue*? (a) 1878, (b) 1901, (c) 1924

22 In which year did Hawaii and Alaska become US states? (a) 1948, (b) 1959, (c) 1963

23 In which year did the following events take place: Yuri Gagarin becomes the first man in space, Rudolf Nureyev defects to the West, and the Berlin Wall is erected?

24 When was the Six-Day War? (a) 1956, (b) 1967, (c) 1973

25 In which year did Richard Nixon resign as US president? (a) 1970, (b) 1972, (c) 1974

26 In which year did Roald Amundsen become the first man to reach the South Pole? (a) 1812, (b) 1864, (c) 1911

27 In which year did the Titanic sink? (a) 1912, (b) 1917, (c) 1919

28 In which year did Spiro Agnew resign over allegations of tax evasion?

29 In which year did Disneyland open? (a) 1955, (b) 1962, (c) 1974

30 In which year did Neil Armstrong become the first man on the moon? (a) 1963, (b) 1969, (c) 1971

31 In which year did the Battle of Britain take place? (a) 1917, (b) 1940, (c) 1945

32 In which year did the following events take place: Civil rights leader Martin Luther King is assassinated, tanks move into Czechoslovakia, and the rock musical *Hair* opens on Broadway?

33 In which year was the Marshall Plan implemented? (a) 1918, (b) 1945, (c) 1948

34 In which year was the Hungarian uprising? (a) 1949, (b) 1956, (c) 1968

35 In which year did Cyprus gain independence? (a) 1960, (b) 1968, (c) 1974

36 In which year did the following events take place: 176 people are killed after riots in Soweto, Jimmy Carter wins the US presidential election, and the hijacking of a French airliner comes to an end at Entebbe airport in Uganda?

37 In which year did the Sharpeville massacre take place? (a) 1922, (b) 1960, (c) 1974

38 In which year were Bonnie and Clyde shot by police after having killed 12 people? (a) 1934, (b) 1952, (c) 1967

39 In which year was King Kong released, and Roosevelt inaugurated as President?

40 In which year was Walt Disney's *Snow White and the Seven Dwarfs* released? (a) 1922, (b) 1938, (c) 1952

41 In which year was Cambodia overrun by the Khmer Rouge? (a) 1975, (c) 1978, (d) 1983

42 Which year saw the reign of three popes? (a) 1966, (b) 1970, (c) 1978

43 In which year was John Lennon shot dead in New York?

44 Which decade is associated with the Jazz Age?

45 Which decade saw the Watergate scandal and the Yom Kippur War?

46 Which year saw the death of Noel Coward and Pablo Picasso? (a) 1973, (b) 1979, (c) 1992

47 When did Margaret Thatcher resign as prime minister? (a) 1986, (b) 1989, (c) 1990

48 In which year did the following events take place: Australia celebrates its becentenary, Reagan and Gorbachev sign the INF Treaty, and Ben Johnson is stripped of his gold medal after having tested positive for drugs?

49 Which year saw a devastating famine in Ethiopia? (a) 1978, (b) 1984, (c) 1988

50 In which year did Eva Peron die? (a) 1952, (b) 1960, (c) 1972

Answers to this quiz are on page 205

The Arts

01 Which of the duo Laurel and Hardy was British by birth?

02 In which year did *South Pacific* first appear on Broadway?

03 Which American musical comedy actress was noted for her 1946 appearance in *Annie Get Your Gun*?

04 For what catchphrase was Bugs Bunny famous?

05 In which year did Mickey Mouse first appear as a comic figure?

06 Who were the owners of the fictional Fresh-Air Taxicab Company of America?

07 When did *Sergeant Pepper's Lonely Hearts Club Band* appear?

08 Which artist was famous for his portrayal of the music halls and cafés of Montmartre?

09 On which island did Gauguin paint some of his finest works?

10 Which musical celebrated an Argentine president's wife?

11 Who played the female lead in the 1937 musical *One Hundred Men and a Girl*?

12 In which film did Greta Garbo utter the famous line, 'I want to be alone'?

13 Who was the female lead in *Jezebel* in 1938?

14 Who said: 'If Mr Vincent Price were to be co-starred with Miss Bette Davis in a story by Mr Edgar Allan Poe directed by Mr Roger Corman, it could not fully express the pent-up violence and depravity of a single day in the life of the average family'?

15 Which British actor made his name playing villains such as Dracula and Dr Fu Manchu?

16 Who is often regarded as the national poet of Scotland?

17 By what fictional name do TV and film viewers recognize Leonard Nimoy?

18 Who wrote *Under Milk Wood*?

19 Which 60s youth hero and singer said: 'I'm glad I'm not me'?

20 What was the name of the Music and Art Fair held in the Catskill Mountains at Bethel, NY, in 1969?

21 Which instrument is Yehudin Menuhin famous for playing?

22 Who is reputed to be the greatest maker of violins?

23 Why is a 'jews harp' so called?

24 The defeat of which military leader is celebrated by the *1812 Overture*?

25 Who painted *Le Déjeuner sur l'Herbe*?

26 'April is the cruellest month, breeding lilac out of the dead land...' From which poem does this come?

27 Who wrote: 'Do not go gentle into that good night... Rage, rage, against the dying of the light'?

28 Which author wrote the *Gormenghast* novels?

29 In which book was the future said to be like 'a boot stamping on a human face – forever'?

30 Who said, 'The only end of writing is to enable the readers better to enjoy life, or better to endure it'?

31 Who wrote *The Red Badge of Courage*?

32 Who played the lead role in *The Bridge on the River Kwai*?

33 Which film, starring Hugh Grant, concerned rites of passage?

34 Daniel Day Lewis starred in which film based on a book by James Fennimore Cooper?

35 Who played the young female lead in *A Room With a View*?

36 Which creatures, invented by Tove Jansson, featured in her series of children's novels?

37 Who was the wizard, created by Tolkien, who befriended dwarves and hobbits?

38 What was the name of the evil lord in *Lord of the Rings*?

39 Name two boys whose evidence saved Muff Potter from the hangman?

40 Gulliver visited a land of giants. What was it called?

41 What novel of the future by Anthony Burgess featured Alex and his droogs?

42 In the film *Bringing up Baby*, who was Baby?

43 Who says of his creator: 'There were things which he stretched, but mainly he told the truth'?

44 In which book does a crocodile swallow an alarm clock?

45 Which jungle-dweller appears in the film *Greystoke*?

46 Which murderous British barber became the subject of a musical?

47 Which heroine of a Swedish children's story is famous for her strength?

48 Which British crime writer was played by Vanessa Redgrave in a film about a mysterious incident in her life?

49 The Osmonds were made up of four brothers and a sister. Who was the sister?

50 What is Meat Loaf's real name?

Answers to this quiz are on pages 205-206

Inventions

01 Who invented the telephone?

02 What did John Logie Baird invent?

03 What function did a polygraph have?

04 Which firm released DOS and Windows, and what is the name of its best-known founder?

05 By what name was the John Gabel Entertainer to become better known?

06 What was the purpose of the Archimedes Screw?

07 Who invented the first mechanical calculating machine?

08 What did Elisha Greaves Otis demonstrate in New York in 1853?

09 The Romans invented hypocaust. What did it do?

10 Who invented the sandwich?

11 Who is thought to be the first person to discover the art of reading silently to oneself rather than reading aloud?

12 Who invented the phonograph?

13 In spite of the sophistication of the ancient Egyptians, what piece of basic technology did they fail to invent?

14 Which people invented the first real paper?

15 In which part of the world was the ice-skate invented?

16 In which country did the longbow originate?

17 What invention revolutionized horse riding?

18 Which human invention was the first object to travel faster than the speed of sound?

19 In 1656 a Dutch mathematician and astronomer invented something which was to revolutionize time-keeping. What was it?

20 What mechanical device did people, especially scientists, use to help with their mathematics before the invention of the pocket calculator?

21 In the late 18th century two Frenchmen – Duchateau and De Chemant – invented something that would be a boon to those with a taste for sweets. What was it?

22 Which spinning machine, named after a girl, was invented by James Hargreaves in 1764?

23 What was Sheffield silver?

24 The Chinese discovered the principle, Leonardo da Vinci designed one, but what was it that Louis Lenormand actually tested himself in 1783?

25 What did Benjamin Franklin invent that helped people who wore glasses?

26 Which French brothers demonstrated a working hot air balloon?

27 What did Samuel Harrison do to help people who wrote with quill pens?

28 Which Scots inventor came up with an improved road surface that was to bear his name?

29 With which invention do you associate the name Alan Turing?

30 With what process would you associate the name Daguerre?

31 Lots of people invented sewing machines that were never popular. Who was the first person to come up with one that was a commercial success (and which still bears his name).

32 Who invented the saxophone?

33 Ascanio Sobrero, who is little known, invented something that was improved by Alfred Nobel, who became famous for it. What was the original invention and why did it do Sobrero so little good?

34 What contribution did William Fox Talbot make to photography?

35 Who invented an electric telegraph that transmitted messages in a code of dots and dashes?

36 Charles Pravaz invented a means of administering drugs that did not require them to be swallowed. What was it?

37 What important photographic process did James Clark Maxwell invent in 1861?

38 What did American farmer James Glidden do to improve the production of barbed wire?

39 What was the first stapling machine used for?

40 The Romans invented the hipposandal. What did it do?

41 Thomas Adams took some chicle and added liquorice flavouring and sold it as Black Jack. What had he invented?

42 Which invention was sold as 'the esteemed brain tonic and intellectual beverage'?

43 Waterman is remembered in connection with the fountain pen, but he did not invent it. What is the connection?

44 The principal ingredient of Aspirin was known to the ancient Greeks. From what was it obtained?

45 Scipione Riva-Rocci invented a device to measure blood pressure. It is still used, but what is its name?

46 How did the military tank get its name?

47 In 1921 it was discovered that insulin, a hormone extracted from the pancreas of pigs, could be used to treat which disease?

48 What was the first product to be made of nylon?

49 What did Percy Shaw invent when he saw his headlights reflected in the eyes of a cat crossing the road?

50 What was the world's first synthetic insecticide?

Answers to this quiz are on page 206

People

01 In which year was John F. Kennedy assassinated?

02 Which movie mogul said: 'That's the trouble with directors. Always biting the hand that lays the golden egg'?

03 Which cartoon character had a girlfriend called Olive Oyl?

04 Whose face reputedly 'launched a thousand ships and burnt the topless towers of Ilium'?

05 Which name connects Woody Allen with Bob Dylan?

06 Who was Russia's 'Mad Monk'?

07 Name a sergeant whose band was made famous by the Beatles.

08 By what name was Marion Morrison better known?

09 Under what name did Samuel Langhorne Clemens find fame?

10 Name the outlaw couple immortalized on film by Faye Dunaway and Warren Beatty.

11 Which Indian political leader was known as 'Mahatma'?

12 Who was the first president of the USA?

13 Which marooned fictional character had a companion called Man Friday?

14 Name the Three Musketeers and their constant companion.

15 Who did Scout, Jem, and Dill want to tempt out of his house?

16 Which black civil rights leader is famous for the phrase, 'I have a dream'?

17 Which boxer was formerly known as Cassius Clay?

18 Which king died at the Battle of Hastings as a result of being shot through the eye?

19 Which Soviet Russian leader took a name which meant 'steel' in his own language?

20 Which 18th-century British explorer was killed by the natives of Hawaii in 1779?

21 Which famous fictional jungle-dweller was created by Edgar Rice Burroughs?

22 With which security organization was J. Edgar Hoover associated?

23 Who is notorious for plotting to blow up the English Houses of Parliament with gunpowder?

24 Which Polish-French woman scientist discovered radium?

25 Who was the constant companion of Tom Sawyer?

26 Which American politician was known as LBJ?

27 Which Mexican General did Davy Crockett and Jim Bowie face at the Alamo?

28 What machine was first manufactured by the gunsmith Philo Remington in 1874?

29 What is O. J. Simpson's full name?

30 Who was the leader of the Free French in World War II?

31 Name the Scottish-born American whose detective agency was famous for solving railroad robberies, spying behind Confederate lines, and strike breaking?

32 What was Henry Deringer famous for inventing?

33 Charles Lutwidge Dodgson was a mathematician. For what was he better known?

34 Which film star was famous for the phrase 'You dirty rat!', even though he never used it in any of his films?

35 Which Hunkpapa Sioux leader is given principal credit for defeating General Custer at the Battle of the Little Big Horn?

36 Who was the pirate, Bluebeard or Blackbeard?

37 By what name was William H. Bonney better known?

38 On which vessel would you expect to find William Shatner and Leonard Nimoy?

39 Which British author wrote gloomily about the year 1984?

40 Which fictional heroine lived in a house with green gables?

41 Who was treated as a giant by the Lilliputians?

42 When a lady told him, 'Sir, you smell!' he replied, 'No, Madam, you smell, I stink'. Who was he?

43 Which name links a South African statesman with the Battle of Trafalgar?

44 Which French heroine was burned as a witch by the English?

45 Which Scottish king defeated the English at the Battle of Bannockburn?

46 Which Italian dictator was known as 'Il Duce'?

47 Sir Edmund Hillary climbed Everest in 1953. Who was his Sherpa companion?

48 Which fictional hero came from the planet Krypton?

49 Which outlaw lived with his Merry Men in Sherwood Forest?

50 Which British scientist discovered gravity, supposedly with the help of an apple?

Answers to this quiz are on pages 206-207

Places

01 Which country would you reach if you crossed the Strait of Gibraltar due south from Spain?

02 On which border is Lake Geneva?

03 What is the name of the Australian island south of Victoria?

04 In which state would you find the Grand Canyon?

05 What was Rock Island used for during the American Civil War?

06 Which country has the world's second largest population?

07 What is South West Africa now called?

08 What is the predominant religion in Mexico?

09 What is the most northerly town in Europe?

10 In which European country did you pay in Schillings?

11 Which is the most southerly point of the UK?

12 Which is New York's largest borough?

13 In which country does the Danube rise?

14 In which city is the Hagia Sofia situated?

15 Which is the only predominantly Moslem state in India?

16 Which country do the Faeroe Islands belong to?

17 In which sea is the Crimea situated?

18 What is the name of the mountain overlooking Cape Town?

19 In which Australian state is Sydney?

20 Which three countries form the Baltic states?

21 In which mountain range is Andorra situated?

22 What is the capital of Indonesia?

23 What is the name of the group of islands off the southern tip of South America?

24 What is the highest mountain in Japan?

25 On which river is Rome situated?

26 In which city can you find St Basil's cathedral?

27 Which town is further north – Oslo or St Petersburg?

28 What is China's largest city?

29 Can you name the three Balearic Islands?

30 In which city can you find the statue of the Little Mermaid?

31 On the border of which two countries does the Principality of Liechtenstein lie?

32 Which Scottish island group do Skye and Iona belong to?

33 What is the name of the strait between the European and Asian part of Turkey, connecting the Sea of Marmara with the Black Sea?

34 What is the capital of Morocco?

35 In which country is the ancient city of Carthage?

36 Which is the most northerly of the Great Lakes in North America?

37 In which city would you find the Taj Mahal?

38 Which is the largest province in Canada?

39 Which is the most sparsely populated state in the USA?

40 Which is the most northerly county in England?

41 In which mountain range would you find the Matterhorn?

42 On which island is Tokyo situated?

43 Which two former African countries formed Tanzania?

44 Where would you find the Prado?

45 What is the capital of Colorado?

46 What island group do Cuba and Jamaica belong to?

47 In which Italian region is Florence situated?

48 Which of the following countries is not in the northern hemisphere: Thailand, Ethiopia, Venezuela, Philippines, Zambia?

49 On which river is Cologne situated?

50 Which country do the Azores belong to?

Answers to this quiz are on page 207

Nature

01 Under what other name is a blueberry also known?

02 Which family does the honeysuckle belong to?

03 Where does the labrador retriever originate?

04 What is a black leopard better known as?

05 What does fly agaric look like?

06 What type of plant is a bladderwort?

07 Where do dragonflies lay their eggs?

08 How do lampreys eat their food?

09 What type of animal is a gharial?

10 Under what name is woodbine also known?

11 What age can a parrot live to?

12 What distinguishes the tenrec from the hedgehog in appearance?

13 What types of tree would you find in the tundra?

14 What do the roots of the scammony plant yield?

15 How many pairs of legs does a centipede have on average?

16 Where do walruses live?

17 In which position do sloths spend the majority of their time?

18 In what type of habitat do gentians grow?

19 What type of animal is an ibex?

20 What do wild pigs use their upturned canines for?

21 Which domesticated animal is the guanaco related to?

22 What sort of animal is the flying fox?

23 How does a chipmunk carry his food?

24 Where do tapirs live?

25 Which is the world's largest land animal after the elephant?

26 What sort of animal is a caribou?

27 What type of vegetation can you find in the taiga?

28 What is a Painted Lady?

29 Which family does the crocus belong to?

30 Which is the largest bird of prey?

31 How does a cheetah bring down its prey?

32 On what type of plant do kiwi fruits grow?

33 What is a syringa also known as?

34 What sort of animal is a marmoset?

35 How does a python kill its prey?

36 Which order does the kangaroo belong to?

37 Where do giraffes live?

38 What sort of animal is a wildebeest?

39 To which family do salamanders belong?

40 What is the name of the insect that transmits malaria?

41 Which type of bear is also called silvertip?

42 The adult male of which monkey has a brightly coloured face and buttocks?

43 Where does the emu live?

44 Which is the largest freshwater fish?

45 What do koalas feed on?

46 What is the name of the insect that transmits sleeping sickness?

47 Do pumas have a spotted skin?

48 Which animal does the okapi resemble?

49 What does a tick feed on?

50 What kind of animal is a chinchilla?

Answers to this quiz are on page 208

Islands

01 Which is the world's largest island?

02 Which island, to the south of Corsica, once belonged to the House of Savoy?

03 An island called the Malagassy Republic was renamed in 1975. What is it now called?

04 On which island does the famous yachting venue of Cowes lie?

05 From which island did the tailless Manx cat originate?

06 By what name was Taiwan formerly known?

07 By what name is the island and holiday resort of Kerkira better known?

08 Which island is infamously linked with the Mafia?

09 What is the large island found in the Gulf of Tongkin?

10 By what name does Argentina, which claims ownership of the territory, refer to the Falkland Islands?

11 Which group of islands would you find north of Crete?

12 Which island lies off the southern tip of India?

13 The ownership of which island is contested by Turkey and Greece?

14 Which islands lie north-east of Cuba?

15 What is the capital of the Philippines?

16 On which 'island' would you relax in Brooklyn, New York?

17 Which island, south of Java, has a festive name?

18 Who was the most famous, though unwilling, resident of the Isle of Elba?

19 The island of Patmos is traditionally considered to be the place where one of the books of the Bible was written. Which one?

20 Which island has been referred to as 'The Pearl of the Antilles'?

21 What is the English name for what the French call the Isles Normandes?

22 The island of Sjelland contains the capital of a European country. Name both the country and the capital.

23 Children are often taught to recognize the map of Italy by looking for a boot kicking a ball. Which island forms the ball?

24 Which island was ceded to France by Genoa in 1768?

25 Which famous peninsula juts into the Black Sea?

26 On which island does the Chinese Nationalist Government hold power?

27 On which island do Malaysia and Indonesia meet?

28 Which group of islands would you find due south of the Bay of Bengal?

29 Of which island group is Mindanao a part?

30 Of which island is Colombo the capital?

31 On which island would you find Larnaka?

32 Which group of islands would you find north-east of Madagascar?

33 Off which continent would you find the Galapagos Islands?

34 On which island other than Britain would you find Suffolk?

35 With which island state do you associate Maui and Oahu?

36 Is Nova Scotia an island?

37 The island of New Guinea is split into two halves. One half is Irian Jaya. Name the other half?

38 By what name were the Hawaiian Islands formerly known?

39 What name is given to a large group of islands?

40 Of what island group is Okinawa a part?

41 Where would you find Kodiak Island?

42 Which country in the Persian Gulf between Qatar and Saudi Arabia is actually an archipelago?

43 Which country lies next to Haiti?

44 What is the capital of Haiti?

45 On which island do Haiti and the Dominican Republic exist side by side?

46 Between which pair of states does the Windward Passage run?

47 What interest did the USA have in Guantanamo, Cuba?

48 Where does the mainland of Great Britain rank in the world's ten largest islands?

49 Which island has a name implying that it has a hard future?

50 The Virgin Islands belong to two countries. What are they?

Answers to this quiz are on page 209

People

01 Who was seduced by the god Zeus in the shape of a swan?

02 Which Greek hero was vulnerable only at his heel?

03 Of which country was Chang Kai-Shek head of state?

04 Which romantic legendary figure later became plain Aircraftsman Ross?

05 Who said: 'Die, my dear doctor, that is the last thing I shall do'?

06 Holmes had his Watson, but who was aided and abetted by Dr Petrie?

07 Pheidippides was famous as the originator of which race?

08 Which blind poet wrote Paradise Lost?

09 Who was the hero of The Catcher in the Rye?

10 Who united Germany by a policy of 'blood and iron'?

11 Which Georgian ran Stalin's secret police?

12 Which queen of the Iceni fought against the Roman invaders of Britain?

13 Name the Roman god of the sea?

14 Which Roman presided over the trial of Jesus.

15 Name the 19th-century French artist who was famous for his small stature?

16 Who is famous for a painting portraying the destruction of Guernica?

17 In which story by J. D. Salinger did Seymour Glass kill himself?

18 Who was the youngest member of J. D. Salinger's fictional Glass family?

19 Who is the odd one out regarding the deaths of the Gandhis: Mohandas, Indira, Sanjay and Rajiv.

20 Name the cyclops of Greek legend.

21 Who was the evil god of Norse legend?

22 Who was the wife of the Indian hero Rama?

23 Which famous doctor was created by Boris Pasternak?

24 Who was the brother of the Anglo-Saxon chieftain Hengist?

25 Who was the Scottish mathematician who invented logarithms?

26 Who was the first Chancellor of post-war West Germany?

27 In the Bible two people are given credit for killing the Philistine Goliath. The most famous was David; who was the other?

28 The skeleton of a man called Yehohanan was discovered in Israel in 1968. What was his unfortunate distinction?

29 For what was Joseph Grimaldi famous?

30 By what name did Archibald Leach find fame?

31 Mr Austerlitz and Miss McMath became partners under other names. What were they?

32 Who was the director of the 1968 film Romeo and Juliet?

33 Who was responsible for inventing dynamite and gelignite?

34 Who pioneered the pneumatic tyres fitted to the Model T Ford?

35 Which Spaniard had delusions of knightly glory?

36 Which explorer was known as 'Il Millioni'?

37 Who was famous for going over Niagara Falls in a barrel?

38 What was unusual about the hanging of John 'Babacombe' Lee?

39 Aleksandr Solzhenitsyn wrote a novel about a day in the life of one man. Who was he?

40 Which Chinese philosopher wrote The Analects?

41 Which Indian political and religious leader defied the British by making salt?

42 Which king of Egypt rejected the old gods and initiated a new form of sun worship?

43 Who was 'mad, bad and dangerous to know'?

44 He was severely disabled and had a speech impediment but became emperor of Rome. Who was he?

45 Who was popularly known as 'The Virgin Queen'?

46 Who brought the Christmas tree to the British?

47 How was Admiral Nelson's body preserved following his death at the Battle of Trafalgar?

48 Who reputedly fell in love with his own reflection?

49 Which legendary ladies were named Medusa, Stheno, and Euryale?

50 Who assassinated Jean Paul Marat?

Answers to this quiz are on pages 209-210

Pot Luck

01 How many googols make a googolplex?

02 What have an outcast group in Japan and a Basque separatist organization got in common?

03 The statue of Eros in Piccadilly Circus, London, commemorates a Victorian reformer. Who was he?

04 The Ngorongoro national park has an explosive connection. What is it?

05 Everyone has heard of the 'waters of Babylon' but which river ran through the city?

06 Soweto, in South Africa, is not an African word. What does it mean?

07 In which film did Gene Kelly dance with an umbrella?

08 What explanation did W. C. Fields give when found reading the Bible on his deathbed?

09 By what name was wartime English broadcaster William Joyce better known?

10 By what name was the European Union originally known?

11 Which Egyptian leader precipitated the Suez Crisis?

12 What is the name of the Israeli parliament?

13 In which country did the Boxer Rebellion take place?

14 What is collagen?

15 What, according to Dante, was the inscription at the entrance to Hell?

16 Who is traditionally considered to have founded Taoism?

17 Apart from its religious merit, what special distinction does The Diamond Sutra possess?

18 What distinction do Edward V and Edward VIII share?

19 Where does Doctor Who come from?

20 Which emperor made his horse a Roman consul?

21 What impossible building task were the Hebrews set by their Egyptian captors?

22 For what purpose was natron used?

23 What is the more polite name for the act of ritual suicide known as hara kiri?

24 What instrument was the precursor of the trombone?

25 Where was the composer Frederick Delius born?

26 Which appropriately named English painter killed his father?

27 Which French mathematician died in a duel at the age of 21?

28 Which religious group worship the Ethiopian emperor Haile Selassie?

29 Would you drink a Molotov cocktail?

30 What did Howard Carter discover in 1922?

31 What inflammatory act was Marinus van der Lubbe accused of in 1933?

32 Which Georgian became known as Uncle Joe?

33 What were kulaks?

34 What notable event took place at Appomattox Court House in 1865?

35 What are the people who follow the teachings of Zoroaster called?

36 Which Spanish naval disaster was commanded by the Duke of Medina Sidonia?

37 For what military blunder was General Galtieri of Argentina responsible?

38 By what name did Siddartha Gautama become well known?

39 For which literary work did Sei Shonagon become famous?

40 Who said: 'Speak softly and carry a big stick'?

41 In which country would you find guerrillas of the Shining Path?

42 In which country did the Red Army Faction operate?

43 What happened at the Battle of Actium in 31 BC?

44 Which English MP was a member of the Hellfire Club?

45 Whose execution prompted Voltaire's remark that the English occasionally shoot an admiral to encourage the others?

46 Why would a Basenji make a poor watchdog?

47 Which pigment does the cuttlefish secrete?

48 What is a haiku?

49 What is a malapropism?

50 Who wrote *Six Characters in Search of an Author*?

Answers to this quiz are on page 210

Classical Music

01 What is the type of 18th century German opera where songs are interspersed with dialogue?

02 How many strings does a cello have?

03 Who orchestrated *Pictures at an Exhibition*?

04 *The Polovtsian Dances* are part of which opera?

05 Who wrote the *Egmont Overture*?

06 What nationality was Béla Bartók?

07 Which instrument does Anne-Sophie Mutter perform on?

08 Which musical work is the *Young Person's Guide to the Orchestra* based on?

09 Which orchestral work is based on *A Thousand and One Nights*, and who wrote it?

10 The *Ode to Joy* is part of which musical work?

11 How many symphonies did Bruckner write?

12 Who wrote the *Reformation Symphony*?

13 Which word describes a vocal and orchestral work telling a sacred story without dramatic effects?

14 What is a bass viola also called?

15 Who wrote the *German Requiem*?

16 Of which musical work is *Anitra's Dance* a part?

17 How many semitones are there in a scale?

18 Who created a catalogue of Mozart's music?

19 Which composer established the 12-tone technique of Serial Music?

20 Who composed *My Fatherland*?

21 Which family does the English horn belong to?

22 How many symphonies did Brahms write?

23 Riccardo Muti is the director of which opera house?

24 Who composed *The Creation*?

25 What is the difference between an interval and a chord?

26 On a piano, what are the strings struck by?

27 In which work would you find a secion entitled *Fortuna Imperatrix Mundi*?

28 By what other name is Mendelssohn's *Hebrides Ouverture* also known?

29 What do you call an interval of eight full tones?

30 Mendelssohn's *Wedding March* is part of which musical work?

31 Who wrote the opera *Russlan and Ludmilla*?

32 Which composer was regarded as the architect of impressionism?

33 Which instrument was Fritz Kreisler famous for?

34 Which was Richard Wagner's only comic opera?

35 What type of instrument did Henry Steinway build?

36 Who wrote *In the Steppes of Central Asia*?

37 What type of singing voice is Elisabeth Schwarzkopf known for?

38 In a tempo direction, what does 'assai' mean?

39 What is unusual about Beethoven's Eighth Symphony?

40 Which country does the polonaise come from?

41 Which instrument does Narciso Yepes perform on?

42 Who wrote *Till Eulenspiegel's Merry Pranks*?

43 What type of singing voice is Dame Janet Baker known for?

44 What is the name given to Beethoven's Fifth Piano Concerto?

45 What is a sarabande?

46 Who wrote *The Swan of Tuonela*?

47 Which three of Verdi's operas are based on plays by Shakespeare?

48 What is the title of Schubert's Fourth Symphony?

49 Which instrument did Arthur Grumiaux perform on?

50 What type of instrument is a sousaphone?

Answers to this quiz are on pages 210-211

Wars and Battles

01 During the conflict in North America, who was defeated in the Seven Years' War?

02 During the French Revolution, which country did France declare war on in 1792?

03 Which army did Napoleon defeat at Austerlitz in 1805?

04 Which two towns saw the first battles of the American Revolution?

05 During the Korean War, which major powers supported the North Koreans?

06 During which war did the Battle of Edgehill take place?

07 The Thirty Years' War was fought on which main issue?

08 Which army was defeated in the Second Battle of Bull Run during the American Civil War?

09 Where was the Spanish Armada fought?

10 Name the coalition headed by Germany, Italy, and Japan during World War II.

11 Who were the Central Powers in World War I?

12 Where was the first battle in the American Civil War?

13 In which year did the USA enter World War I?

14 Who was the German Field Marshal who commanded the Afrika Korps in North Africa during World War II?

15 What did the Russian February Revolution achieve?

16 In which year did the Vietnam War start?

17 In which year did the USA start sending troops to Vietnam?

18 What was the opposing branch of Russian socialism that was in conflict with the Bolsheviks before and during the revolution?

19 Which general led the Union army in the Battle of Fair Oaks in the American Civil War?

20 In which year did the Battle of Trafalgar take place?

21 The French Revolution started during the reign of which king?

22 Which treaty ended the Seven Years' War?

23 During the American War of Independence, where did the British troops finally surrender?

24 Where was Robert E. Lee's army defeated on July 3 1863 in the American Civil War?

25 In which war was poison gas first used successfully?

26 What part of Egypt was captured in the Six Day War?

27 What was the codename of the US bombing campaign during the Vietnam War?

28 Name of the major offensive of the Vietcong and North Vietnamese troops on South Vietnamese cities in 1968?

29 Which war did the Treaty of Vereeniging end?

30 Which state was created as a result of the First Balkan War?

31 What was the name of the German statesman who provoked the Franco-Prussian War?

32 What was the aim of the Boxers during their uprising in 1900?

33 During which war did Hannibal invade Italy?

34 Which commander, during the American Civil War, led Union troops toward Richmond?

35 Who were the three colonial powers in North America at the start of the Seven Years' War?

36 During the Napoleonic Wars, which army was defeated at Friedland?

37 During which war did the Battle of Lutzen take place?

38 Where did the Confederate Army surrender at the end of the American Civil War?

39 Which French king was captured at the Battle of Poitiers during the Hundred Years' War?

40 What was the location of a major evacuation of British and French troops by British ships and boats in 1940?

41 Which war started on the Jewish Holy Day of Atonement in 1973?

42 During which battle were tanks first used?

43 What were the disputed areas in the Russian-Japanese War?

44 In which year did the first Russian Revolution begin when troops fired on workers marching towards the Winter Palace of the czar, and what name was given to the day?

45 When was the Boer War?

46 What did the Balkan League try to achieve during the First Balkan War?

47 Which city was destroyed during the Third Punic War?

48 During which war did the Battle of Sluys take place?

49 What was the name of the peninsula at the entrance to the Dardanelles that British troops and their allies tried to capture in World War I?

50 What was the location of Henry V's victory over an army of French knights in 1415?

Answers to this quiz are on page 211-212

Science

01 What shape is an amoeba?

02 Name the steroid hormones produced by the ovaries.

03 An elementary particle is often described with the words 'charm', 'beauty', and 'strange'. What is it?

04 What is an elementary particle carrying a unit charge of negative electricity called?

05 A colourless, odourless, and tasteless inert gas, it emits a bright-red glow when conducting electricity in a tube. What is it?

06 If you mixed saltpetre (75%), sulphur (10%), and charcoal (15%), what would you get?

07 Which explosive chemical is also used as to treat heart disease?

08 What is the medical name given to a severe paroxysmal pain in the chest associated with an insufficient supply of blood to the heart?

09 What medical name is often given to the pit of the stomach?

10 What is the medical name for the small tube projecting from the large intestine into the lower right abdominal cavity?

11 What is the name for the fine, powder-like material produced by the anthers of seed plants?

12 What happens to atmospheric pressure as altitude increases?

13 Name the lines on a weather map that connect points of equal atmospheric pressure?

14 Which branch of science deals with the atmosphere of a planet?

15 What is the technical name for a low-lying cloud formation occurring in extensive horizontal layers with rounded summits?

16 What name is given to the rapid decrease in atmospheric pressure that results in the release of nitrogen bubbles into body tissues?

17 What is the technical name for a reinforced spherical deep-diving chamber used to study oceans?

18 What do we call the substance that hardens and strengthens the cell walls of plants?

19 Name the condition in which a diseased part of the body thickens and hardens.

20 What is the process by which organisms of different species cohabit to their mutual advantage?

21 What is special about the temperature -273.17° Celsius (-459.67° Fahrenheit)?

22 What is the name given to the inevitable and steady deterioration of a system?

23 Which seventeenth-century scientist and mathematician wrote the *Principia Mathematica*?

24 Who was the first scientist to predict the return of a comet?

25 Find a word which is commonly used in pathology, dentistry, and mathematics.

26 What name is given to a pathological stony mass found in the stomach?

27 Who was the first scientist to use a telescope to study the stars?

28 Which Polish astronomer proposed the theory that the Earth and other planets revolve around the sun?

29 Name the Greco-Egyptian mathematician who theorised that the Earth was at the centre of the universe.

30 Who invented the cathode ray tube?

31 Who invented the miner's safety lamp?

32 Which American invented the machine-gun?

33 For what is William Henry Fox Talbot famous?

34 Which inventor operated from laboratories at Menlo Park and West Orange?

35 Who was the Englishman with whom Edison competed to invent the electric light bulb?

36 Who developed the revolver?

37 Which American developed vulcanized rubber?

38 What have the first adding machine and *The Naked Lunch* got in common?

39 Which nation is credited with the invention of the wheelbarrow?

40 In which year do you think the glass mirror was invented: (a) 567 BC, (b) 1278 AD, or (c) 1563 AD?

41 The Dewar vessel was the precursor of which common household object?

42 What is the chief industrial use of nitric acid?

43 What class of organic compounds responsible for growth and repair of tissue in animals is obtained from foods such as meat, fish, eggs, milk, and legumes?

44 By what other name was the Smilodon known?

45 Which gas was discovered by Joseph Priestley?

46 What is hypoxia?

47 The compound sold as Malathion is used for what purpose?

48 What is 'absolute alcohol'?

49 By what common name is diacetylmorphine known?

50 Name a group of nerve cells that form a nerve centre.

Answers to this quiz are on page 212

Books

01 The character Natty Bumpo has two nicknames, one English and the other French. What are they?

02 What scandalous tale was written by Lucius Apuleius?

03 What novel by Richard Adams was devoted to the adventures of a group of rabbits?

04 What was the name of Ray Bradbury's tale of an evil travelling fair?

05 Which of Anthony Burgess's novels concerned early Christianity?

06 Most people know only the film of *Breakfast at Tiffany's*, but who wrote the novel?

07 What is the name of the series of novels for which Anthony Powell became famous?

08 Name David Lodge's novel concerning a catastrophe at a well-known British institution.

09 Sinclair Lewis wrote a novel about an evangelical preacher. What was the title?

10 What dangerous-sounding novel was written by Laclos?

11 Who wrote the novels in which the spy George Smiley appears?

12 Name the British professor who wrote a novel apparently opposing cannibalism.

13 In which Graham Greene novel did he describe small-time crooks at a seaside resort?

14 Which F. Scott Fitzgerald hero had a past cloaked in mystery?

15 Which of Christopher Isherwood's Berlin characters was noted for her emerald green nail polish?

16 Which novelist walked out on a midsummer's morning and had cider with a girl called Rosie?

17 What was the real name of Ettrick Shepherd?

18 Which of Stephen King's characters used psychokinetic powers to gain revenge?

19 Ruth Prawer Jhabvala had parents of two nationalities but was born in a third country. Can you name all three?

20 Who created the detective Lord Peter Wimsey?

21 Which Nigerian novelist wrote *The Famished Road*?

22 Which American scholar wrote a series of books on the mythologies of the world, entitled *The Masks of God*?

23 Which Robert Louis Stevenson novel used characters reminiscent of Robin Hood and his merry men?

24 What name was given to a series of four books by Lawrence Durrell set in Egypt?

25 What event was dramatized in John Masters' novel *The Night Runners of Bengal*?

26 What was Bram Stoker's occupation at the time he wrote *Dracula*?

27 What brief book did Stephen Hawking write?

28 In which science fiction novel, written by which scientist, do we read of an intelligent cloud?

29 Who wrote a book entitled *The Unbearable Lightness of Being*?

30 In which American novel, and by which author, did Mrs Robinson appear?

31 In which book, with a floral title, are monks murdered by means of a poisoned book?

32 In a J.D. Salinger book a story is dedicated 'For Esme'. What is the rest of the dedication?

33 Which novel, in the form of two diaries, tells the story of a girl held prisoner by an entomologist?

34 Which Frenchman wrote about a revolution in New York?

35 Who wrote *The Naked Ape*?

36 Which writer created the character Captain Nemo?

37 Who wrote a book entitled *Ethics*?

38 Who wrote *Utopia*?

39 For what literary work is Cellini chiefly remembered?

40 Name the US town made famous by Garrison Keillor.

41 Which science fiction story tells the story of a laboratory mouse and a mentally subnormal human?

42 Which psychiatrist wrote the book *Games People Play*?

43 Which Asimov novel starts by stating the Three Laws of Robotics?

44 What was the name of the walking, carnivorous plants created by John Wyndham?

45 In which Norman Mailer novel is the protagonist mummified?

46 A book called *The English Governess at the Siamese Court* was turned into a musical. What was it called?

47 Which novel, with a Chinese connection, was written by Simone de Beauvoir?

48 Which Graham Greene novel was set in French Vietnam?

49 Who wrote *The Descent of Man*?

50 Who wrote: 'The mind is its own place, and in itself can make a heav'n of hell, a hell of heav'n'?

Answers to this quiz are on pages 212-213

Popular Music and Musicals

01 Who recorded the album *Hounds Of Love*?

02 Who was the organist with The Doors?

03 What was the name of Paul McCartney's group after the break-up of the Beatles?

04 Who wrote the musical *Candide*?

05 Which song contains the words 'Behind the shelter in the middle of a roundabout the pretty nurse is selling poppies from a tray'?

06 What was Abba's first US hit single?

07 Who wrote the piece *In the Mood*?

08 Which original Queen album contains the song *Bohemian Rhapsody*?

09 Who sang the title song to the film *Hello Dolly*?

10 Which ragtime song was used in the film *The Sting*?

11 Which song contains the words 'Take me on a trip upon your magic swirlin' ship, my senses have been stripped'?

12 On which original Dire Straits album is the song *Walk of Life*?

13 From which musical comes the song *Mr Mistoffelees*?

14 What was Madonna's first hit?

15 Who sang the title song to the film *What's New Pussycat*?

16 In which year did Elvis Presley die?

17 Which Carole King album topped the charts in 1971 and went on to sell over 15 million copies?

18 Who wrote the score to the musical *Evita*?

19 Who was the singer of the *Eurythmics*?

20 Which song contains the words 'Sitting on a sofa on a Sunday afternoon, going to the candidates' debate'?

21 Who wrote the song *The Times They are a-Changin'*?

22 What was the theme song to the film *Flashdance*?

23 In which musical can you find the song *Food, Glorious Food*?

24 On which Fleetwood Mac album is the song *Go Your Own Way*?

25 Who wrote the operetta *The Mikado*?

26 Who preceded Phil Collins as lead singer of Genesis?

27 What was the title of the first Beatles single?

28 Who wrote the score to the musical *Kiss Me Kate*?

29 Which song contains the words 'Beelzebub has a devil put aside for me'?

30 Who wrote the song *This Land is Your Land*?

31 From which musical does the song *There's no Business like Show Business* come from?

32 Who was the lead singer of The Police?

33 Who played the king in the film musical *The King and I*?

34 Who made the single *Peggy Sue*?

35 What was Bon Jovi's first top ten hit?

36 Who sang the theme song to the James Bond film *Goldfinger*?

37 For which type of music was Bob Marley famous?

38 Who made the album *Tubular Bells*?

39 Who made the recording *Banana Boat Song*?

40 Who brought out the album *The Joshua Tree*?

41 Which song contains the words 'My father was a tailor, he sewed my new blue jeans'?

42 Who was the lead singer of T. Rex?

43 From which musical does the song *All I Ask of You* come ?

44 Which Parisian singer was known for songs like *Non, je ne regrette rien*?

45 What was Elton John's first US top 10 hit?

46 Who wrote the music to the film musical *Gigi*?

47 Which two singers had a massive hit in 1985 with the remake of *Dancing in the Street*?

48 Through which film did Meat Loaf become a success?

49 Who is the singer of U2?

50 Who first performed the rock opera *Tommy*?

Answers to this quiz are on page 213

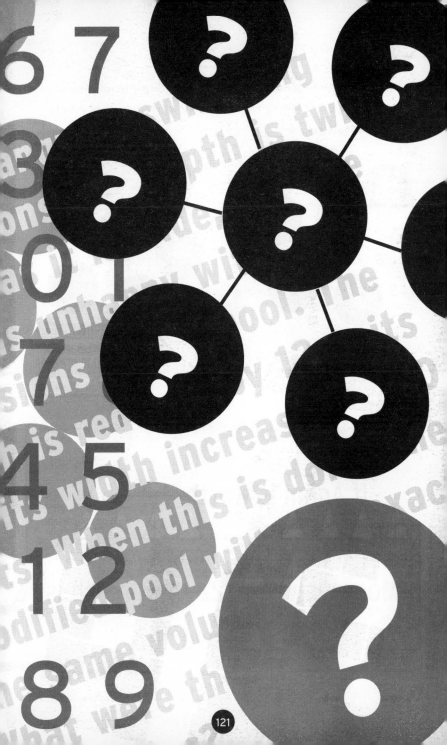

Insert the missing numbers. In each pattern the missing
number has something to do with the surrounding numbers
in combination.

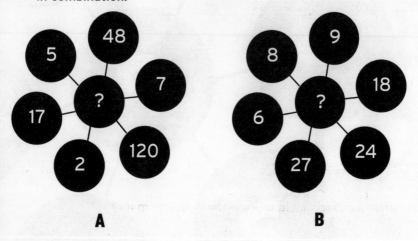

A   **B**

See answer page 214

If Agam is worth 13, Dali is worth 17, Degas is worth 18 and Monet is worth 22, how much is Raphael worth?

See answer page 214

What number should replace the question mark?

6	5	0	6	8	*25*
?	9	5	3	6	
2	4	5	7	8	*26*

13   10   16   22

See answer page 214

What number should replace the question mark?

○ + ○ - ○ = 6

- + ○ = 3

x ○ x ○ = 140

○ + ○ + ○ = ?

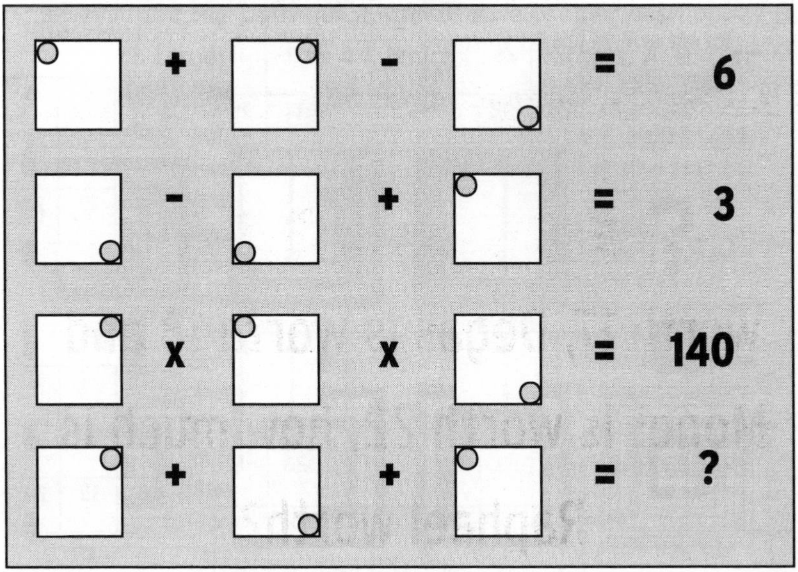

See answer page 214

Za-za is older than Fifi, but younger than Juan. Fifi is older than Jorjio and Maccio. Maccio is younger than both Carlos and Jorjio. Juan is older than both Fifi and Maccio, but younger than Carlos. Who is the eldest, and who is the youngest?

C
J
Z
F
J
M

See answer page 214

NUMBER PUZZLES   PUZZLE 6

When the shaded sections of this puzzle are brought together, one of the white patches is inserted into the middle to make a magic square in which all rows, columns and long diagonals add to 49.

Is it patch A, B, C or D?

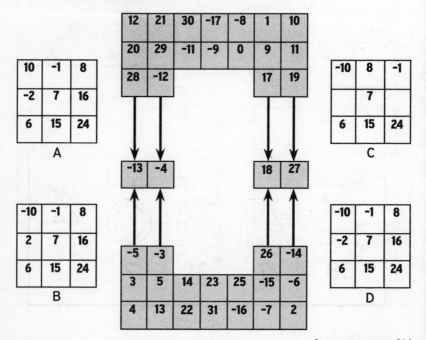

See answer page 214

A rectangular swimming pool of constant depth is twice as long as it is wide, but the owner is unhappy with the dimensions of the pool. The length is reduced by 12 units and its width increased by 10 units. When this is done, the modified pool will hold exactly the same volume of water. What were the pool's original dimensions?

See answer page 214

Each shape is made up of two items, and each same shape has the same value, whether in the foreground or background.

What number should replace the question mark?

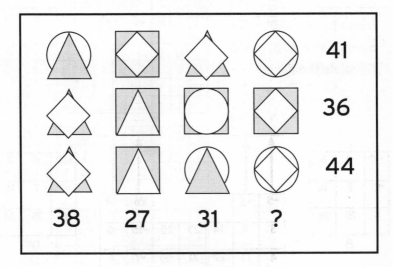

See answer page 214

What is the area of the shaded path, if the path is one unit wide?

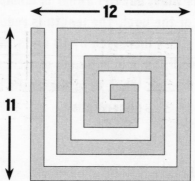

See answer page 214

The panel on the right, when complete, contains the binary numbers from 1 to 25. Does binary patch A, B, C or D complete the panel?

1	1	0	1	1	1	0	0	1	0	1
1	1	0	1	1	1	1	0	0	0	1
0	0	1	1	0	1	0	1	0	1	1
1	1	0			?			1	1	1
0	1	1						0	0	1
	0	0						0	1	0
0	1		1	0	1	0	0	1	0	1
0	1	1	0	1	1	0	1	0	1	1
	1	1	0	0	0	1	1	0	0	1

1	0	1	1	1
1	1	1	1	0
1	1	1	0	0

A

0	1	1	0	1
1	1	1	0	0
0	1	0	0	1

B

	1	0	1	1
1	1	0	1	1
0	0	1	0	1

C

0	1	1	0	1
1	1	1	0	0
1	1	0	0	1

D

See answer page 214

Which letters, based on the alphanumeric system,
should go into the blank boxes?

6	1	7	3		5	1	3	9		2	2	9	2			
1	3	5	4	A H B	2	8	6	4	F B C	4	3	0	9			
7	7	0	9		8	6	2	6		7	1	7	8			

See answer page 214

What number, when you multiply it by 5
and add 6, then multiply that result by 4
and add 9, gives you a number that,
when you multiply it by 5
and subtract 165, gives you a number that,
when you knock off the last 2 digits,
brings you back
to your original number?

See answer page 214

What number should replace the question mark?

289

256 ◄   ► 196

225

441

? ◄   ► 324

361

See answer page 214

Present at Juan's birthday party were a father-in-law, a mother-in-law, a daughter-in-law, two sons, two daughters, two sisters and a brother, four children, three grandchildren, two fathers, two mothers, a grandfather, and a grandmother. However, family relationships can be complicated.
One man's brother can, of course, be another man's brother-in-law, and at the same time, someone's son.
With that in mind, what is the smallest number of people needed at the party for the above relationships to exist?

See answer page 214

How many rosettes are missing from the blank circle?

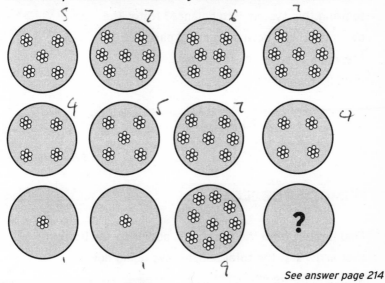

See answer page 214

Forty people took part in a freestyle race. Twenty people ran. Ten people dashed. Five people bolted and sprinted. Three people bolted, dashed, ran and sprinted. Two people ran, bolted, and sprinted. Five people ran and sprinted. Two people dashed, ran, and sprinted. How many people neither dashed, ran, bolted, nor sprinted?

See answer page 215

What value needs to go into the upper box
to bring this system into balance? Note: The
beam is broken down into equal parts and
the value of each box is taken
from its midpoint.

?

18

See answer page 215

Find a route from the top of this puzzle to the bottom
that arrives at the total 353, always going down and to an
adjoining hexagon.

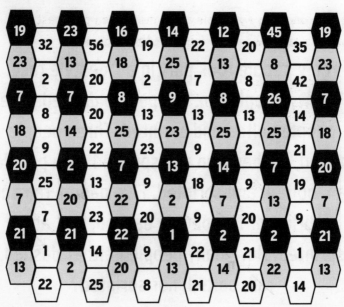

See answer page 215

Using only the numbers already used, complete this puzzle to make all the rows, columns, and long diagonals add to 27.

6				
			2	
	9			
				3
		7		

See answer page 215

At 3pm one day, a flagpole and a measuring pole cast shadows as shown. What length is the flagpole?

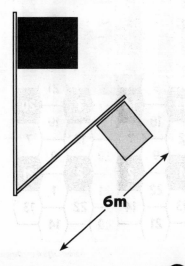

6m

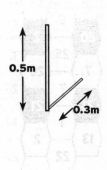

0.5m

0.3m

See answer page 215

Use logic to discover which shape has the greatest perimeter.

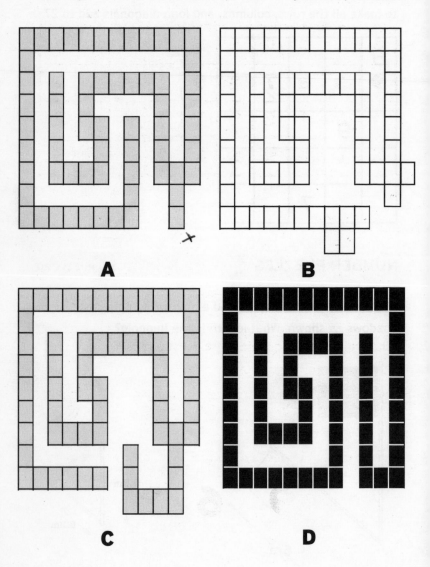

A

B

C

D

See answer page 215

NUMBER PUZZLES — PUZZLE 22

Crack the code to find the missing number.

A	B	C	D	E	F	G	H	I	J
9	3	8	7	8	9	2	8	5	7
1	2	1	5	?	7	1	0	1	2
K	L	M	N	O	P	Q	R	S	T

See answer page 215

NUMBER PUZZLES — PUZZLE 23

What number should replace the question mark?

6 8 4 8 7

9 6 ?

See answer page 215

What number replaces the question mark?

What is the value of each animal?

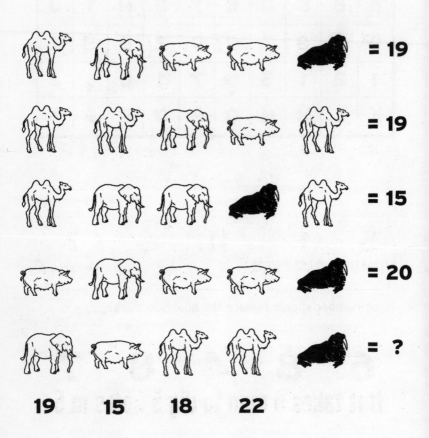

19   15   18   22

See answer page 215

NUMBER PUZZLES — PUZZLE 25

What number should replace the question mark?

A	B	C	D	E
3	11	7	4	18
2	12	7	5	19
5	17	11	6	?

See answer page 215

NUMBER PUZZLES — PUZZLE 26

If it takes 5 men to dig 5 holes in 5 hours, how many men does it take to dig 100 holes in 100 hours?

See answer page 215

Put the right number in the blank star.

See answer page 215

If you buy 9 barrels of beer for 25 Credits each, but you are given a 25% discount on the last 4 barrels, and you are given in change 3 times the cost of all the barrels less half the value that your discount would be if your discount were 25% more for the last 2 barrels than the discount you were actually given, what was the total cost of the barrels?

See answer page 215

When a ball is dropped from a height of 9m, it bounces back two-thirds of the way. Assuming that the ball comes to rest after making a bounce which takes it less than 2mm high, how many times does it bounce?

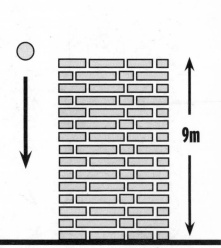

9m

See answer page 215

The planet Pento is inhabited by a race of highly intelligent one-toed quadrupeds with elephant-like trunks. So with four toes and a trunk, they have adopted the five base for their number system. With that in mind, convert the Pento number 1234 into its decimal equivalent.

See answer page 215

Each same shape has the same value. What number should replace the question mark

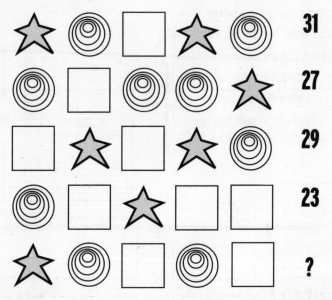

See answer page 215

Find the missing number.

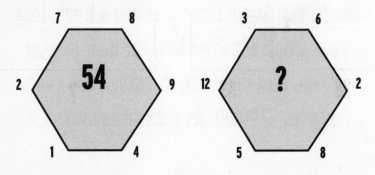

See answer page 216

What three-digit number should replace the question mark?

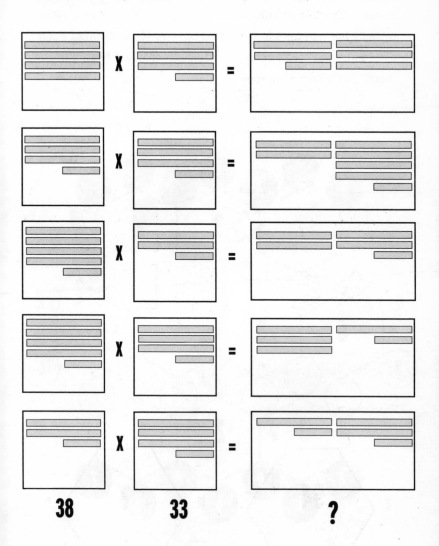

38　　　**33**　　　**?**

See answer page 216

The three balls at the top of each hexagon should contain numbers that, when added together and subtracted from the total of the numbers in the three balls at the bottom of each hexagon, equal the number inside each relevant hexagon. Insert the missing numbers.

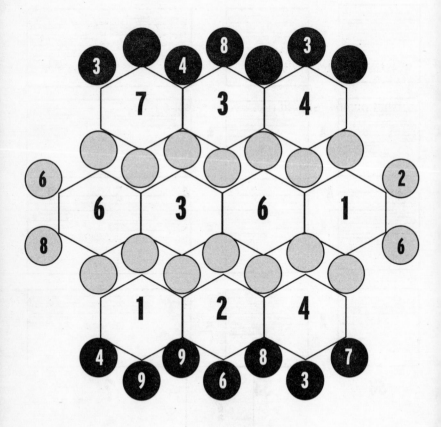

See answer page 216

What number, when added to a number 10 times as big, gives a number that, when its right-hand digit is multiplied by four and added to the result of the above, gives 1000?

See answer page 216

What number should replace the question mark?

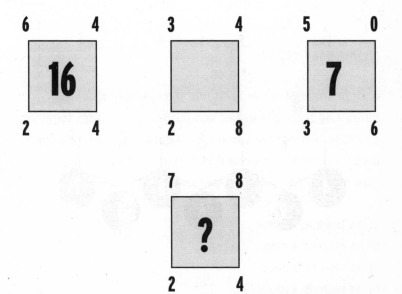

See answer page 216

This clock has been designed for a planet that rotates on its axis once every 16 hours. There are 64 minutes to every hour, and 64 seconds to the minute. At the moment, the time on the clock reads a quarter to eight. The hands will meet at eight o'clock. To the nearest second, what time will it be when they next meet after that?

See answer page 216

A large sheet of paper is 0.1 mm thick. A man amuses himself by tearing it in half and putting both pieces together, and then tearing those into four sheets, and repeating the process until he has done it twenty-five times.

How high is the stack of paper now?

a) As thick as a book

b) As high as a man

c) As high as a house

d) As high as a mountain

See answer page 216

This is a time puzzle. Which symbol is missing ?
Is it A, B, C, D, E or F?

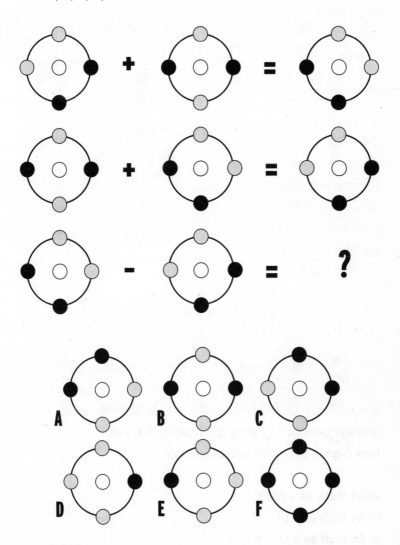

See answer page 216

Which number should replace the question mark?

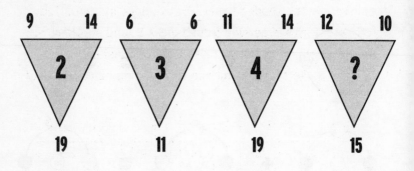

See answer page 216

What number should replace the question mark?

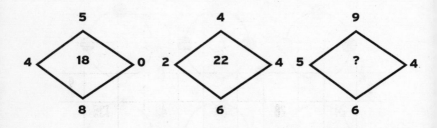

See answer page 216

In the boxes at the corner of each shaded number-square, insert the digits which are multiplied together to give the numbers in the shaded boxes. For example, in the bottom left corner, 144 is derived from 3 x 6 x 8 (and another multiplier – here 1), but you also have to consider how this helps to make solutions for the surrounding numbers... and so on.

3		5		4		4		3		3
	90		120		64		144		54	
2										1
	48		96		16		72		36	
1										2
	160		80		20		150		30	
4										1
	180		10		40		100		15	
9										3
	27		8		32		12		81	
3										9
	24		28		84		45		135	
8										1
	144		42		63		225		25	
3		6		1		3		5		1

See answer page 216

Each like symbol has the same value. Supply the missing total.

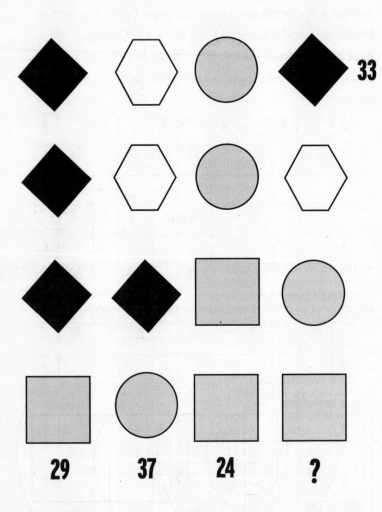

See answer page 216

What time will it
be, to the nearest
second, when the
hands of this clock
next appear to
meet?

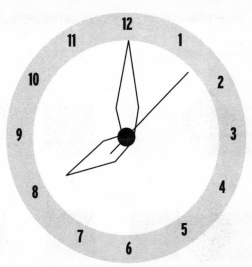

See answer page 216

What number should replace the question mark?

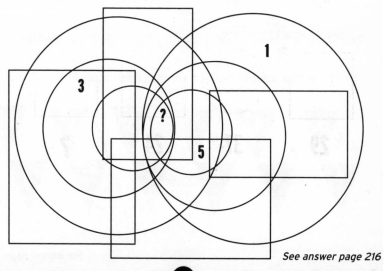

See answer page 216

Insert the missing numbers in the blank hexagons.

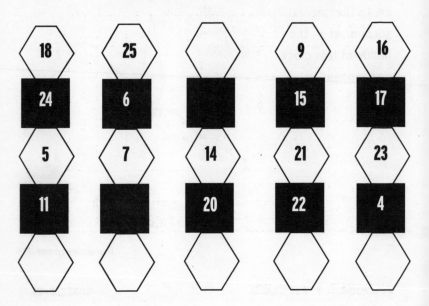

See answer page 216

What number should replace the question mark?

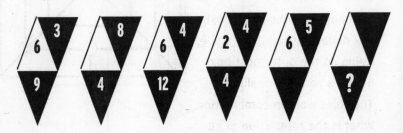

See answer page 217

What number should replace the question mark?

9	7	2	5	7	4	3	2	5	1
									4
9	4	5	2	7	5	2	7		5
3							9		9
6		?	2	6	5	1	8		8
2									1
8	3	5	2	7	4	3	3	6	5

See answer page 217

Black counters are nominally worth 4.

White counters are nominally worth 3.

Being on a diagonal trebles a counter's value.

Being on or in the innermost box doubles a counter's value.

Being on the outermost box halves a counter's value.

The rules work in combination.

What is the total value of all the counters on the board?

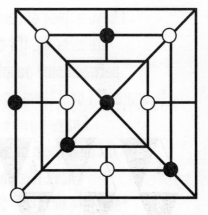

See answer page 217

What number continues the sequence?

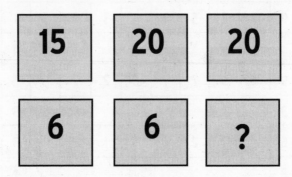

See answer page 217

I have a deck of cards from which some
are missing. If I deal them equally
between nine people, I have two cards
to spare. If I deal them equally between four people,
I have three cards to spare.
If I deal them between seven people,
I have five cards to spare.
There are normally 52 cards in the deck.

How many are missing?

See answer page 217

Each same symbol has the same value. What number should replace the question mark?

$$\left(\text{⬡} \times \text{▲} \right) + \text{◆} = 26$$

$$\left(\text{⬡} + \text{▲} \right) - \text{◆} = 9$$

$$\left(\text{⬡} - \text{▲} \right) - \text{◆} = 3$$

$$\left(\text{⬡} + \text{▲} \right) \times \text{◆} = \text{?}$$

See answer page 217

What number should replace the question mark?

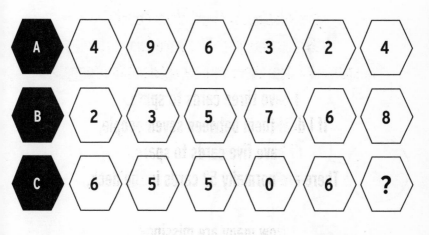

A	4	9	6	3	2	4
B	2	3	5	7	6	8
C	6	5	5	0	6	?

See answer page 217

What number should replace the question mark in the blank square?

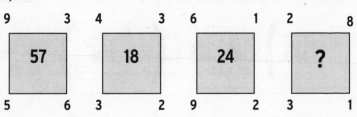

9   3   4   3   6   1   2   8

| 57 | 18 | 24 | ? |

5   6   3   2   9   2   3   1

See answer page 217

Insert the central numbers.

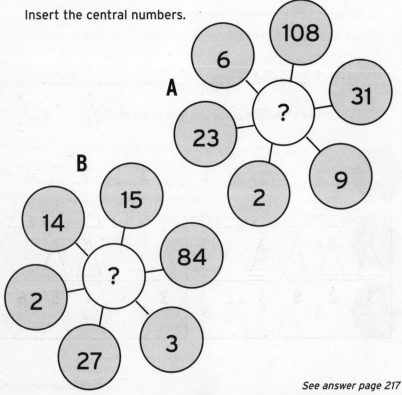

See answer page 217

What number should replace the question mark?

See answer page 217

NUMBER PUZZLES

PUZZLE 57

The symbols represent the numbers 1 to 9.

Work out the value of the missing multiplier.

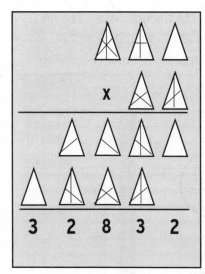 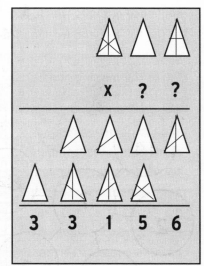

See answer page 217

This system is balanced. How heavy is the black box (ignoring leverage effects)?

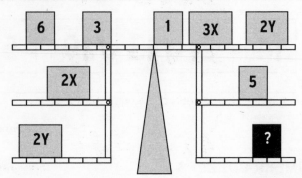

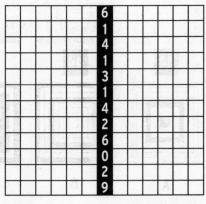

See answer page 217

Somewhere within the large number below left, there is a sequence of digits which, if put into the grid below, starting at the top left and working from left to right, row by row, will give the middle column as shown when the grid is completed. Put in the missing numbers.

3095867235697809123948
5668094164162223456341
2191836216144432708 9298
4615295500162193200025
2813121585871939450 4639
5123161762113267792 28965
6123102238404612898 540
4326161425261609341 7285
8300912428596481342 568
30998012847306133 9021

			6				
			1				
			4				
			1				
			3				
			1				
			4				
			2				
			6				
			0				
			2				
			9				

See answer page 217

$$2 \times \sqrt{2} = \sqrt{8}$$

$$3 \times \sqrt{5} = \sqrt{45}$$

What number should replace the question mark?

$$4 \times \sqrt{6} = \sqrt{?}$$

See answer page 217

The black, white and shaded rings of this square target always have the same value, irrespective of their position, and each target is worth 44. Which of the targets, A, B, C or D, will replace the question mark?

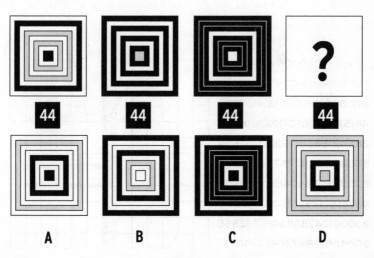

See answer page 217

How many different ways is it possible to arrange the order
of these four kings?

See answer page 217

Previous to the time shown, when
were all four of these same digits
last on display on this watch?

See answer page 217

If the top left intersection is worth 1, and the bottom right intersection is worth 25, which of these nodule grids, A, B, C or D, is worth 67?

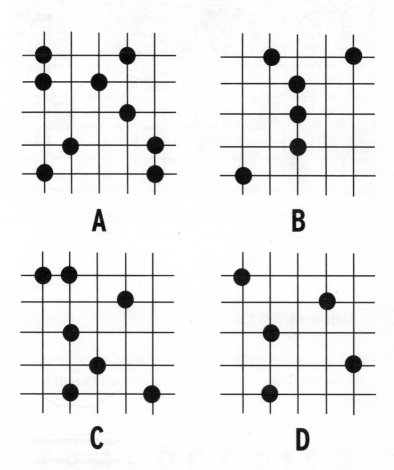

A

B

C

D

See answer page 218

Each similar shape has the same value. Which is the missing symbol?

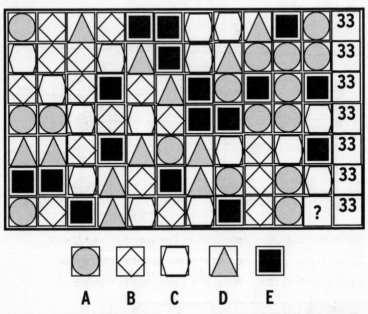

A   **B**   **C**   **D**   **E**

See answer page 218

NUMBER PUZZLES

PUZZLE 66

Within the number below, find two numbers, one of which is double the other, and which when added together make 10743.

57162383581

See answer page 218

This system is balanced. How heavy is the black weight (ignoring leverage effects)?

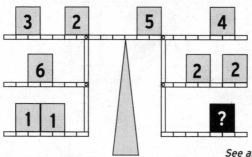

See answer page 218

There are logical differences in the way each of these squares work, but they all involve simple addition or subtraction of rows. What are the missing numbers?

A

2	6	3	0	8	a
3	8	0	3	9	b
2	3	?	5	7	c
1	9	2	5	4	d
2	1	5	3	6	e

B

2	1	3	2	0	a
1	3	5	6	2	b
0	5	?	4	7	c
2	9	6	3	0	d
1	0	2	9	9	e

C

3	1	2	0	9	a
6	1	4	6	2	b
2	8	?	1	9	c
4	9	6	5	7	d
7	1	3	3	3	e

D

3	3	6	4	7	a
3	3	6	1	1	b
1	1	?	2	0	c
3	4	1	0	6	d
2	1	9	3	2	e

See answer page 218

TUNNEL

A

B

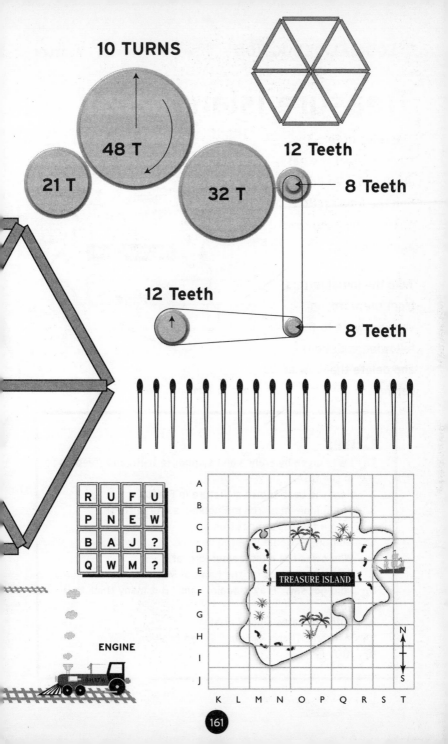

10 TURNS

48 T

21 T

32 T

12 Teeth

8 Teeth

12 Teeth

8 Teeth

R	U	F	U
P	N	E	W
B	A	J	?
Q	W	M	?

ENGINE

TREASURE ISLAND

N
S

A B C D E F G H I J

K L M N O P Q R S T

Treasure Island

The rules of this treasure hunt are easy; all you have to do is find the intersection point of the open row and column.

Take the initial letters from the words in your answers to the following questions and delete that row or column.

Clues

1. I was given by France and symbolize truth and freedom in the USA.
2. I am the best-known structure in France.
3. The female monarch in England is one of these.
4. I am a famous puppet frog.
5. Goldfinger would love to live here.
6. Who owns the multi-coloured coat?
7. Scientist famous for the Laws of Motion.
8. I did not say, "Play it again, Sam." But many think that I did.
9. Suffix to dates since Christ.
10. Margaret Thatcher held this top position.
11. 100.

See answer page 219

The Swiss Deposit Code

A man carried a code for his Swiss account engraved in the buckle of his belt until he died. He did not pass on the secret to his family, but in his will he stated that whosoever cracked the code could have the contents of the safe deposit box in the Swiss bank. Can you crack the code?

```
DID   =   IIF
BAD   =   AG
CCE   =   ACCB
HEG   =   DBCC + GG
No        F - C - G - B
          OPENS THE BOX
```

See answer page 219

Take a Second Look

This is a series of letters in common use. Can you determine the next in the sequence?

N, W, H, O, I, I, ?

See answer page 219

Train the Train Driver

A rail depot had an oval track with two branch lines. This was used
to train drivers in unusual conditions. The teacher gave them the
following problem on the blackboard:

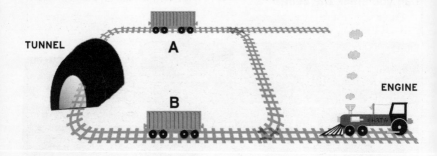

Move load A to position B and load B to position A without the
load going through the tunnel and return the engine to its starting
position. How did the trainee drivers do this?

See answer page 219

Square Metres?

If the perimeter of a rectangular field was 3000 metres, what would be the maximum area that you could contain within that perimeter if you could reorganize it into any configuration?

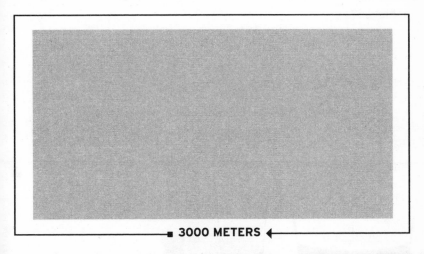

3000 METERS

See answer page 219

Fact or Fiction

The early Roman calendar originated in the city of Rome about 7 to 8 centuries before the Christian era. It was supposedly drawn up by Romulus, brother of Remus, in the February of his 21st year. Today modern historians dispute the validity of this. Do you know why?

See answer page 220

Moving Water Uphill

You are given a dish of water, a beaker, a cork, a pin, and a match. You have to get all the water into the beaker. You cannot lift the dish of water or tilt it in any way, and you cannot use any other implement to move the water into the beaker. How is this achieved?

water

See answer page 220

Secret Messages

A journalist had been recruited by a foreign power to find out the chemicals being used in a top secret project. He was not given any contact name to pass the information on to. He was told to disguise the chemicals within a note in the personal column in the newspaper on April 1st and they would crack his code and obtain the knowledge. Only the journalist knew how he would transmit the message and the code he would use, but the foreign power knew that the message contained the name of 1 gas and 6 other elements or chemicals. The message was contained in the following text:

> Jacob – Alter August's trip to Germany
> to the unfair one on the Nile.

Can you find the hidden information?

See answer page 220

Mysteries of Time

A young man proclaims, "The day before yesterday I was 17, but I will be 20 next year." How?

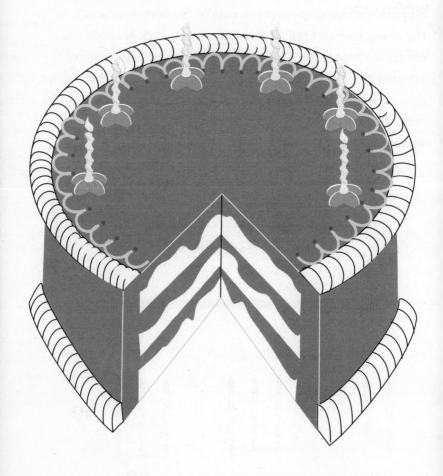

See answer page 220

Logical Thinking with Matchsticks

Is this possible?

By removing 4 matchsticks can you rearrange those left so that the perimiter rows and colums still come to 9 matches each?

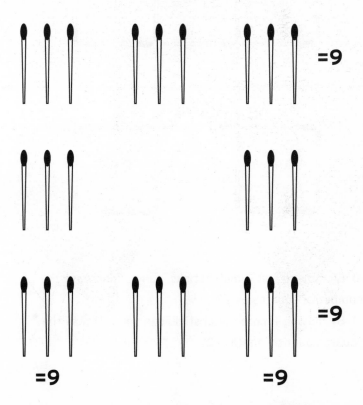

=9

=9

=9

=9

=9

See answer page 220

More Matchstick Trickery!

Only the most devious of lateral thinkers will be able to solve both parts of this. Can you?

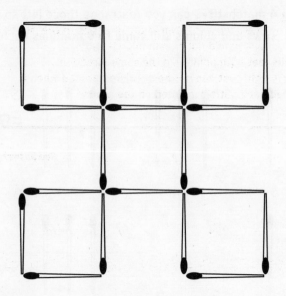

a) By moving just 2 matchsticks, can you increase the number of squares by 2?

b) By moving 1 more matchstick, can you increase the square count by another 2?

See answer page 220

Front Foot Forward

A man's right foot was facing due north and his left foot after one pace was pointing south. How was this possible?

Clues

1. The one pace was taken in the direction of the right foot and he did not turn in mid-stride.
2. His feet both pointed in the same direction.
3. His right foot had not been twisted around when it had been initially planted on the ground.

See answer page 220

LOGICAL DEDUCTION PUZZLE 13

Triangles

What is the largest number of non-overlapping triangles that can be produced by drawing 7 straight lines?

See answer page 220

Logical Deductions of Who or What Am I?

1. What am I?

Sometimes I am one before I'm one.

When I'm under one I, and others like me, are given the same name.

Males and Females have different titles.

When I am over one but remain young these names change.

Between the ages of one and two males and females can also be given the same name.

When I am fully grown I am called another name.

All through my life people give me a name that is personal to me.

I am well known in the sporting world, although I always have to share credit.

I am eight and male.

2. Who am I?

I am deceased, but my name and actions are well known.

I was a leader of my people but I never had a crown.

I was often upset with my people and they were sometimes upset by me.

I passed on messages and rules.

I warned people of death and destruction.

My most famous work was in stone.

See answer page 220

3. What am I?

I have been around for over a thousand years, but my appearance and format have changed with time.

I have been mechanical in construction in one form up to the present day and in electromechanical form since the 1930s.

I have been miniaturized in my current form and I am used by almost all schoolchildren and adults alike.

You have counted on me to help you for years.

4. What am I?

I give birth, but I am the male of the species.

I am covered by consecutive rings of body armour.

I have a long tubular snout and live in warm waters.

My eyes can work independently of one another.

I am not a mammal.

5. What am I?

I am a ballroom dance.

I became popular in the 1940s in Western Europe and the USA.

I have simple forward and backward steps with tilting and rocking body movements.

I am danced to in 4/4 time with syncopated rhythm.

My point of origin in S. America would give my name away too easily.

I am a happy dance that is very popular in my country of origin.

See answer page 220

A Waiter's Lot Is Not a Happy One

A waiter is serving vegetables to 51 diners in a hotel. There are peas, carrots, and cauliflower. Two more diners want peas and carrots only than those who wanted just peas. Twice as many people want peas only as cauliflower only. 25 diners do not want cauliflower, 18 diners do not want carrots, and 13 diners do not want peas. Six diners want cauliflower and peas but no carrots.

a) How many diners want all three vegetables?

b) How many diners want cauliflower only?

c) How many diners want two of the three vegetables?

d) How many diners want carrots only?

e) How many diners want peas only? *See answer page 220*

The Train Driver

You are driving a train. It stops at Milton Keynes and 25 people board it. It then goes to Leicester where 55 people get on and 43 get off. The next stop is Nottingham where 3 people get off and only 1 gets on. The train continues its journey, making Doncaster its next stop, where 19 get on and 13 get off. The next stop is York, which is the final destination. The driver then gets off the train also, and looks in the mirror in the washroom. What colour eyes does the driver have?

No clues for this one. It should be easy.

See answer page 220

Cleaning Confusion

At a dry-cleaner's one more customer brings in a jacket only, than trousers only. Three times as many people bring in trousers, jacket, and a skirt as bring in a skirt only. One more person brings in a jacket and a skirt but no trousers, than brings a skirt and trousers but no jacket. Nine people bring in trousers only. The same number of customers bring in a jacket only, as do trousers and a skirt but no jacket. 32 customers do not bring in a skirt and 24 customers do not bring in a jacket.

a) How many customers bring in all 3 of the items?
b) How many customers bring in only 1 of the 3 items?
c) How many customers bring in a jacket only?
d) How many customers bring in 2 of the 3 items?
e) What is the total number of customers bringing in any of the 3 items?   *See answer page 221*

A Lewis Carroll Gem

The Governor of Kgovjni wished to give a very small dinner party, and invited his father's brother-in-law, his brother's father-in-law, his father-in-law's brother, and his brother-in-law's father. What is the minimum number of guests invited?

See answer page 221

Word Connections

In each of the following sentences, a group of related words are hidden. These words can be found by looking at the end of one word somewhere in the sentence and connecting it to the beginning of the next word. What are the related words in each sentence?

1. The ballot usually takes no more than half an hour, then the fun begins. The hi-fi attachments are in place for David's party. In the fridge there is a large samosa above the sandwiches and a chocolate gateau diagonally placed on the shelf below to give more space.

2. If anything is wrong with the replica shirts then management must be informed so that they can combat escalating problems.

3. While Grandfather sang an impromptu ballad, the wood on the campfire began to char perfectly and Grandmother joyfully recited age-old rumours.

4. According to forces protocol, Lieutenant Barnabas settles the cashbox error and ensures the young soldiers' faces will be agleam.

5. The cream beret that I managed to drop all through the mud at the Mexico rally has been dry-cleaned and should now appear

See answer page 221

Confusing Paper Model

Using a rectangular piece of paper can you make the model shown? You can make 3 straight-line cuts to the paper and the paper model must not be glued or held together with clips.

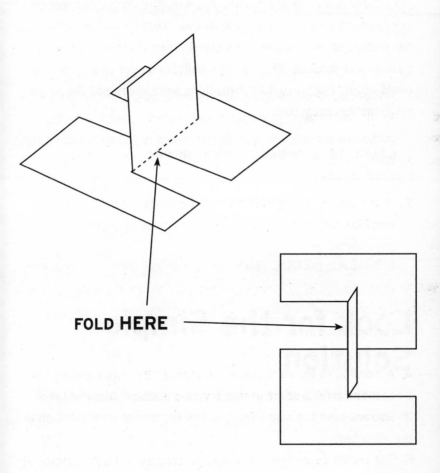

FOLD HERE

See answer page 221

Confusing Family Relations

1. Alice, who had returned from Australia, wished to meet all of her relations, so she organized a reunion. She invited her mother, her mother's sister-in-law, her sister, her sister's mother-in-law, her mother-in-law's sister, her sister-in-law's mother and her next door neighbour. What is the smallest number of people that could attend the party if all invitations were accepted? No illegal relationships permitted.

2. A family has 5 children, of which half are boys. How can this be?

See answer page 221

Look for the Simple Solution

What is the final product of this series of multiplications if all of the letters have the same value as the number of their position in the alphabet?

$(t - a)(t - b)(t - c) .... (t - z)$

See answer page 221

The Mississippi Gambler

The professional gambler only played dice, but he had made his own. He had 3 coloured dice, and each colour had 3 numbers, which were each on 2 faces.

The Red Die :	2 - 4 - 9 - 2 - 4 - 9	(total 30)
The Blue Die :	3 - 5 - 7 - 3 - 5 - 7	(total 30)
The Yellow Die :	1 - 6 - 8 - 1 - 6 - 8	(total 30)

The dice had not been loaded with weights. The gambler always let his customer have the choice of colour, then he would choose his. It was always a game for only 2 players and the object was to have the highest number on any roll.

This worked very well for him. He always seemed to have an edge. Can you work it out so that by the law of averages he always had a better than 50 : 50 chance, and can you state what the real chances of his winning were?

See answer page 221

The Fairground Game

At a fairground game, players had 3 darts each to attempt to win a teddy bear, a board game, or a beer glass. There were 4 winners of teddy bears and games, not but glasses. Two more people won both a glass and a teddy bear but no game, than those who won a glass and a game but no teddy bear, 43 of the prize-winners did not win a teddy bear, and 48 of the prize-winners did not win a game. Nine people won both a glass and a teddy but no game, and 31 people did not win a glass. 74 people won at least one prize.

a) How many people won a teddy bear only?

b) How many people won all 3 prizes?

c) How many people won a glass only?

d) How many people won 2 prizes only?

e) How many people won a game only?

See answer page 221

So You Think You're Good at Maths?

Can you rearrange the following addition to make an answer of 100? You can use each number only once but you can add any mathematical symbols you wish.

6 1
1 8

See answer page 221

The Striptease Artist

The man called the striptease bar from his home and asked for a particular entertainer to go to his room for a private session. He paid her to visit him. After one hour the man said that he really enjoyed what she did, and he felt much better. The man was the manager of the bar, and afterwards was able to work. Why?

Clues
1. She was only required to remove a few clothes.
2. The entertainer was between 18 and 20 years old.
3. She was not there for her beauty.

See answer page 222

The Car Problem

When you are moving forward in your car, are there parts of the car that appear to be going backward while being attached to the car?

See answer page 222

Dozy Policemen

A small boy was riding his bicycle around the housing estate where he lived. He went up and down roads that had no outlets, in and out of trees, up and down the curbs. Unfortunately, he took a sharp turn and the front wheel of his bicycle hit a curb. The small boy fell from his bicycle and was knocked unconscious. Fortunately, there was a policeman at the scene of the accident. You would have thought that an ambulance might have been called, and all details of the accident and statements taken from anyone who witnessed the accident. Why was this not done?

See answer page 222

Decimated

In Roman times, soldiers who were to be punished were forced to form a line, and every tenth one was executed. This is the origin of the word "decimate". If you were one of 1000 soldiers lined up in a circle, with every second soldier being executed until only one remained, in which position would you want to be in order to survive?

See answer page 222

Children's Age

A man has 9 children born at regular intervals. The sum of the squares of their ages is equal to the square of his own. What are the ages of the children?

See answer page 222

Random Chance

You have been blindfolded and asked to put a red sock in to the red bag, a blue sock into the blue bag, a white sock into the white bag, and a yellow sock in the yellow bag. The 4 bags and 4 socks are correctly coloured. What are the odds that you can get exactly 3 of the 4 matched first time?

See answer page 222

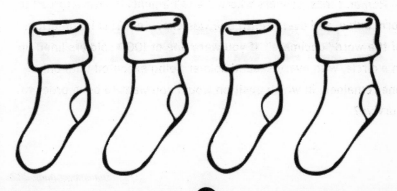

That & This

Add 'This' to 'That', divide by 3.
The square of 'This', you'll surely see.
But 'That' to 'This' is 8 to 1.
So figure what they are for fun.

See answer page 222

The Warehouse Sale

I went to a warehouse sale and bought 3 lots of tee-shirts. The total cost was £260. Each lot was at a different price and a different size. In each lot the individual price of the tee-shirts in pence was the same as the number of tee-shirts in the lot. If I bought 260 tee-shirts can you tell me the lot sizes?

£ £ £ £ £ £ £ ?

See answer page 222

The Rector Total

If each letter is substituted for a single-digit number in this sum, can you determine what the value of each letter should be?

```
    C E L L A R
    C O R P S E
    C O L L A R
      C L O S E
        C A S E
        C O P S
+ _____
    R E C T O R
```

See answer page 222

Cocktail Sticks

1. By moving only 3 of the cocktail sticks in the shape below, can you make 4 equal triangles? All of the cocktail sticks must be used.

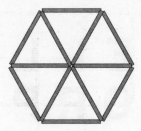

2. By moving only 3 of the cocktail sticks in the shape below, can you make 7 triangles and 3 diamond shapes?

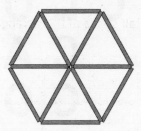

3. Using 6 matchsticks of equal length, create a shape with 4 equilateral triangles.

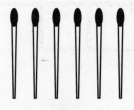

See answer page 222

4. By moving only 2 cocktail sticks, can you rearrange the shape below so that you will be left with 8 squares of the original size?

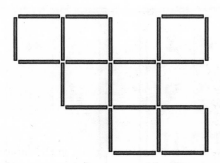

5. By moving 2 cocktail sticks in this arrangement, can you form 15 squares?

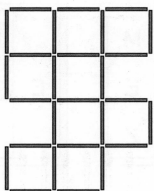

See answer page 222

Rotations

Using the logic of the first grids, complete both of the incomplete grids.

a.

10	18	3
7		9
2	4	11

	4	
11		18
	3	

b.

T	D	M
L		E
K	U	Z

	U	
E		T
	Z	

See answer page 223

Complex Numbers & Letter Grids

Can you find the missing numbers or letters from the grids below?
The rules used in the completed grids, in each case, will give you
the rules for the incomplete grids.

1.

	A	B	C	D	E	F
a	7	9	6	5	3	3
b	4	6	3	7	0	3
c	9	2	4	1	1	4
d	5	8	2	7	2	6

7	7	5	6	1	9
4	9	6	6	0	0
3	5	1	9	0	6
8	9	4	6	?	?

2.

	A	B	C	D
a	F	D	N	V
b	J	I	O	Z
c	M	Q	H	Q
d	G	A	L	Y

R	U	F	U
P	N	E	W
B	A	J	?
Q	W	M	?

3.

	A	B	C	D	E	F
a	7	9	6	5	3	3
b	4	6	3	7	0	3
c	9	2	4	1	1	4
d	5	8	2	7	2	6

7	7	5	6	1	9
4	9	6	6	0	0
3	5	1	9	0	6
8	9	4	6	?	?

4.

	A	B	C	D
a	F	D	N	V
b	J	I	O	Z
c	M	Q	H	Q
d	G	A	L	Y

R	U	F	U
P	N	E	W
B	A	J	?
Q	W	M	?

See answer page 223

Changing Words

Changing only 1 letter and making a new word each time, can you find the shortest routes between the 2 given words to change the first word into the second word? The letter order may not change.

1.	SEAT	-	TRAM	(3 steps)
2.	HEAD	-	TAIL	(4 steps)
3.	STONE	-	BRICK	(7 steps)
4.	WHITE	-	BLACK	(7 steps)
5.	HERE	-	JUNK	(5 steps)
6.	FAIR	-	RIDE	(6 steps)
7.	WRITE	-	CARDS	(5 steps)
8.	BROWN	-	TREES	(4 steps)
9.	GLASS	-	CHINA	(6 steps)
10.	GREEN	-	BLACK	(6 steps)

See answer page 223

Magic Squares

Can you complete these 2 magic squares so that each of the following items totals 34? You must use each of the numbers 1-16 once only.

The rows across	= 34
The columns down	= 34
The cross diagonals	= 34
The centre 4 numbers	= 34
Each corner block of 4 numbers	= 34

1)

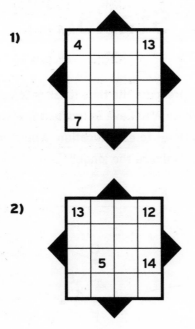

2)

See answer page 223

Extinct?
I Don't Think So

Can you think of an animal, which, if it were made extinct and all of its DNA were also destroyed, could still repopulate itself in under 2 years?

See answer page 223

The Fire Station Location

The drawing below represents the time it takes to go between towns for the fire engine. You have to locate a fire station that minimizes the travel times to each location. Where would you locate the station to minimize the longest journey?

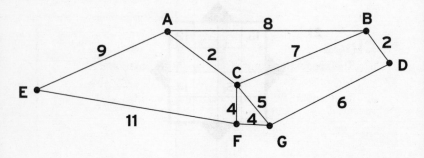

See answer page 223

The Rabbit Family

How many male and female rabbits are there in a family if each male has 1 fewer female relatives than he has male relatives, and each female has 2 males fewer than twice the number of female relatives she has?

See answer page 223

Strange But True!

Prior to the American Civil War two famous people challenged each other to a duel. When the seconds had been selected the weapons were chosen. Pistols were suggested, but one of them objected saying that this was most unfair to him. One of the duellists was much taller and was therefore a larger target, whereas the other was a smaller target. How was this resolved?

Clues

1. The suggestion came from the shorter man and his seconds.
2. They could still fire at the same time and in the traditional way.
3. They were both given only one shot.

See answer page 223

The Gearbox

The gearbox below consists of 4 gearwheels with intermeshing gears and two pulley belts, or drive belts. If the large 48 tooth gearwheel rotates exactly 10 times in a clockwise direction, in what direction will the pointer be facing on the gearwheel at the bottom of the arrangement, and how many times will it rotate?

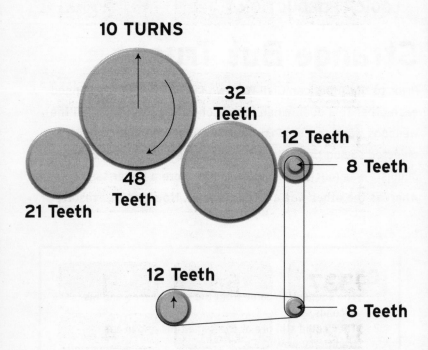

See answer page 223

Links?

What numbers should replace the question marks?

8752	4524	1080
6978	5382	4346
7388	6424	?

7628	5126	3020
9387	6243	1088
8553	2254	?

9337	56	-1
8725	62	4
4821	?	-5

See answer page 223

ANSWERS

Answer 1 is M, go to 11. In alphabetical order you go four places forward and then two back.

Answer 2 is Wet Wet Wet. The letters are jumbled up. W is the 23rd letter.

Answer 3 is 18. The consonants are worth 6, and the vowels are worth 3. 18 + 7 = 25.

Answer 4 is No, go to 19. Amazing – but true.

Answer 5 is D, go to 20. The letters spell Mississippi.

Answer 6 is 9. The number of letters in each number is spelled out. Five has 4 letters, six has 3 letters, sixteen has 7 letters and twenty-six has 9 letters. 9 + 18 = 27.

Answer 7 is D, go to 22. The number of elements increases by two at each step, but D increases by only one.

Answer 8 is 2. The numbers in each circle add up to 8. 2 + 14 = 16.

Answer 9 is No ways, go to 3. There will always be at least one line crossing with another.

Answer 10 is 48. The vowels are worth 8, and the consonants are worth 4. 48 - 33 = 15.

Answer 11 is 15. 48 candles make 12 new ones but these 12, when burnt, will make a further 3. 12 + 3 = 15. 15 + 9 = 24.

Answer 12 is L. Bill Clinton is the name. L is the 12th letter. 12 ÷ 2 = 6.

Answer 13 is Spider, go to 17. A spider has 8 legs. All the others are insects, which have 6 legs.

Answer 14 is 54. All the other numbers are squares (e.g. 2 x 2 = 4, 3 x 3 = 9, 7 x 7 = 49, 9 x 9 = 81). 54 - 24 = 30.

Answer 15 is 139. At each stage the new bottles, when finally broken, will make more new bottles. 279 ÷ 3 = 93. 93 ÷ 3 = 31. 31 ÷ 3 = 10 (with 1 left). 10 ÷ 3 = 3 (with 1 left). 3 ÷ 3 = 1. Take this one and add the two others left to make another 3. So, again, 3 ÷ 3 = 1. 93 + 31 + 10 + 3 + 1 + 1 = 139. 139 - 131 = 8.

Answer 16 is Italy. The others are Europe and Asia. Italy is a country, but the other two are continents. I is the 9th letter. 9 + 12 = 21.

Answer 17 is 74. Double the first number, add three, double the next number, add three, etc. 74 – 43 = 31.

Answer 18 is Whale, go to 26. It is the only mammal; the others are all fish.

Answer 19 is 131, go to 29. It is the only odd number.

Answer 20 is 26. Vowels are worth 2 and consonants are worth 5. 26 – 19 = 7.

Answer 21 is 4. He makes three from the original nine, and another one from the remains of the three. 4 + 14 = 18.

Answer 22 is 26. The sequence here is add 5, add 1, add 5, add 1, etc. 26 ÷ 2 = 13.

Answer 23 is Sun, go to 10. The sun is a star, the others are all climatic conditions.

Answer 24 is Above, go to 4. The numbers above the line, when written as words, all contain the letter E.

Answer 25 is 25. The sequence here is add 3, add 4, add 3, add 4. 25 + 3 = 28.

Answer 26 is 23. All the others are multiples of 7. 23 – 14 = 9.

Answer 27 is H. The letters are the first of ten, twenty, thirty, etc., and hundred is next. H is the 8th letter. 8 – 3 = 5.

Answer 28 is 22. Explanation. 200 makes 20, and from the 20 he will get another 2. 22 – 8 = 14.

Answer 29 is 14. 14 – 12 = 2.

Answer 30 is Above, go to 12. All numbers above the line, if spelled out, are three-letter words.

Answer 31

Will you see Tocsin live? The path you should have taken is:

1	11	24	4
19	29	2	23
10	15	8	16
21	18	26	9
3	25	28	14
30	12	6	27
5	20	7	22
13	17	31	

Between 26 and 27, you ought to have visited 9, 3, 25, 28, 14, 30, 12 and 6.

All together, that gives an answer of **180**.

1. IN THE DIRT

One child fell on his feet, and his face was not covered with dust to make his face dirty. When he saw his friend's face covered in dust, he thought his own must also be dirty; the other boy only saw the first boy's clean face. The dirty child therefore did not think that he needed to wash.

2. THE HOLIDAY DISASTER

Bill Drallam (Mallard backwards) was a duck. They flew in front of a plane during lift-off and entered the engine intake, causing the plane to crash. The plane might have survived if only one or two ducks flew into the engine, but several birds were hit and drawn into other engines.

3. EVOLUTION

Animal x on island A was an ass. Animal y on island B was a horse. Animal z on island C was a donkey.

The new animal on island B was a MULE (ass/mare). The new animal on island C was a HINNEY (donkey/stallion).

4. THE FULL CASK OF WINE

He washes some small pebbles and sand with the fresh water, and puts the washed and dried materials into the bottle. He then puts the bottle-neck into the bunghole. The pebbles and sand will fill into the cask to be replaced by wine into the bottle.

5. RECOVERING WITH A LETTER

A piece of paper with the letter 'A' on it. The instructions said, "If you add 'A' to 'her,' you will have 'hear.'"

6. THE TWINS CAUSE CONFUSION

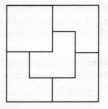

7. HOW TO TRICK THE GENIE?

Aladdin chose one envelope, and without opening it, tore it up into lots of pieces, and asked the king to read what option he had rejected in the other envelope.

8. CAR GRID

After going forward, you reverse.

The Earth (40-43)

1 The crust.
2 Geology.
3 Fossils.
4 Geography.
5 No.
6 The core.
7 70%.
8 Antarctica.
9 A volcano.
10 A crater.
11 A hole in the Earth's crust spouting fountains of boiling water.
12 An eruption.
13 The magnitude of an earthquake.
14 Tsunami.
15 A mountain.
16 Lines of latitude.
17 Lines of longitude.
18 Erosion.
19 Scree.
20 Up.
21 A swallow-hole.
22 The covering of the land by ice during an ice age.
23 A large 'river' of slowly moving ice.
24 A cold period in the Earth's history when the ice sheets are much larger than today.
25 A fjord.
26 A pile of debris left by moving ice.
27 Permanently frozen ground.
28 A narrow neck of land projecting into the sea.
29 A beach.
30 It has no tides.
31 A coral reef.
32 An island.
33 Tide.
34 An especially high or low tide.
35 The atmosphere.
36 Nitrogen.
37 The trapping of heat by gases in the atmosphere.
38 An instrument for measuring atmospheric pressure.
39 An instrument for measuring temperature.
40 Wind.
41 Pressure.
42 Fog (or mist).
43 The amount of water vapour in the air.
44 Hurricane.
45 No.
46 A dark, liquid fossil fuel formed from tiny plants and animals.
47 A solid fossil fuel made from the remains of plants.
48 Methane.
49 Green.
50 Gold, silver, and platinum.

Pot Luck (44-47)

1 Exactly the same amount.
2 Crab.
3 (c) Ceres.
4 Albino.
5 A dice game.
6 (d) patience.
7 The water lily.
8 (b) a painter.
9 (a) an opera.
10 The jumbo jet.
11 (b) Boeing.
12 Sails.
13 (c) Elvis Presley.
14 The north wind.
15 Switzerland.
16 Washington DC.
17 (c) Sweden.
18 Basketball.
19 The are both called kids.
20 Cygnets.
21 Goslings.
22 An artificial language.
23 The Quakers.
24 Lemmings.
25 (b) rhubarb.

ANSWERS

26 True.
27 (c) a jellyfish.
28 (d) Scotland.
29 A fish.
30 Florida.
31 Peking.
32 (c) Korea.
33 The Pope.
34 In the roof.
35 A deep, narrow valley or gorge worn by running water.
36 Because light travels in straight lines.
37 Evens (ie 50-50).
38 Egypt.
39 Seventy.
40 A semi-precious stone.
41 An allergic reaction to pollen.
42 China.
43 Five loaves and three fish.
44 Spain.
45 A horse.
46 Hieroglyphs.
47 A shade of blue.
48 A lucky accident.
49 Astrology is an attempt to predict events by observation of the stars. Astronomy is the scientific observation of all cosmic phenomena.
50 The Great Bear.

Synonyms (48-51)

1 (a) animated.
2 (b) gloomy.
3 (a) make.
4 (b) toil.
5 (a) keen.
6 (c) brotherly.
7 (b) bizarre.
8 (b) generous.
9 (a) memento.
10 (b) flawless.
11 (a) witty.
12 (b) understandable.
13 (b) mysterious.
14 (a) dark.
15 (a) handy.
16 (b) spoken.
17 (a) several.
18 (c) strong.
19 (a) delicate.
20 (b) contented.
21 (b) caught.
22 (b) improbable.
23 (a) bravery.
24 (b) require.
25 (a) change.
26 (b) crack.
27 (c) stroke.
28 (a) ask.
29 (c) part.
30 (b) make.
31 (b) honourable.
32 (a) arrange.
33 (c) continual.
34 (a) amount.
35 (c) inquiry.
36 (a) specimen.
37 (b) disloyalty.
38 (c) thankless.
39 (a) beat.
40 (b) crave.
41 (a) perfect
42 (b) beastly.
43 (a) condense.
44 (b) hang.
45 (b) acquire.
46 (c) often.
47 (b) wrestle.
48 (a) listen.
49 (a) envy.
50 (a) depart.

Nature (52-55)

1 Moths move around at night, and have hair-like or feathery antennae, stout bodies, and a frenulum that holds the front and back wings together.
2 Toads are more terrestrial and have a broader body and rougher, drier skin.
3 The cat family.
4 The dog.
5 In the Antarctic.
6 In the Arctic.
7 The potato.

8   Crows.
9   The Great White.
10 The science of classification.
11 Frog spawn is laid in a jelly-like mass, toad spawn is laid in strips like tape.
12 The cuckoo.
13 An Australian wild dog.
14 A domestic animal that has returned to the wild.
15 The emu.
16 The cat.
17 No. They are usually warning other birds to keep out of their territory or trying to attract a mate.
18 No. Fish extract oxygen from the water by the use of gills.
19 Yes, but only over short distances. The horse is fastest over long distances but, surprisingly, humans are faster over very long distances.
20 No. It's an animal.
21 Cold-blooded.
22 Yes. Some species can, for example, use a thorn to pick grubs out of cracks.
23 They are arachnids.
24 They are crustaceans.
25 To warn other creatures to keep away.
26 The female.
27 A fish.
28 The female.
29 Rats and the fleas which lived on them.
30 A fruit.
31 Flying south for the winter.
32 No. Seagulls have become skilled scavengers and many live inland almost permanently.
33 No. Its brain is actually very small.
34 The skunk.
35 The wolverine
36 They are all types of miniature orange.
37 A crane fly.
38 The poppy.
39 A fungus that grows symbiotically with algae.
40 The hyena.
41 In the USA or China.
42 Mainly, but they eat meat when they can get it.
43 A cygnet.
44 An elver.
45 Scarab.
46 Yes.
47 Daisy.
48 Heather.
49 A small freshwater fish with spines along its back.
50 Porcupine fish.

The Human Body (56-59)

1   Skin.
2   The skeleton.
3   The heart.
4   The kneecap.
5   True.
6   The gums.
7   Twenty.
8   Vertebrae.
9   The eye.
10 The large and small intestines.
11 The Adam's apple.
12 No.
13 The throat.
14 Dentine.
15 About 70 beats per minute.
16 True.
17 The gall bladder.
18 The sternum.
19 In the forearm.
20 Urine.
21 Pores.
22 It prevents it from clotting.
23 Molars.
24 Melanin.
25 In the mouth.
26 Flakes of skin from the scalp.
27 Arthritis.
28 (c) capillaries.
29 Short-sightedness.
30 In the lower leg.
31 Lungs.

32 (a) eulogy.
33 Nerves.
34 Incisors.
35 The ear.
36 The diaphragm.
37 A jelly-like liquid called aqueous humor.
38 The brain.
39 The pelvis.
40 To reduce body temperature.
41 In the arm.
42 The membrane covering the brain.
43 Mumps.
44 (c) pachyderm.
45 Digestion.
46 Respiration.
47 In the buttocks.
48 The semi-circular canals.
49 An ulcer.
50 Cholesterol.

Opposites (60-63)

1 (c) disinterested.
2 (a) thankless.
3 (a) mean.
4 (b) free.
5 (b) superficial.
6 (c) industrious.
7 (a) imaginary.
8 (b) relaxed.
9 (a) extant.
10 (c) decrease.
11 (c) earnest.
12 (c) partial.
13 (b) delectation.
14 (b) vacuous.

15 (c) fascinating.
16 (a) barren.
17 (b) purchase.
18 (b) listless.
19 (b) advance.
20 (a) dull.
21 (b) noisy
22 (c) cheerful.
23 (c) disperse.
24 (b) clever.
25 (a) promote.
26 (c) sour.
27 (b) free.
28 (c) descend.
29 (b) civilized.
30 (a) esteem.
31 (b) discreate.
32 (b) pessimistic.
33 (b) antagonist.
34 (a) dissonance.
35 (b) dismantle.
36 (c) dearth.
37 (a) extraneous.
38 (b) friendly.
39 (a) blunt.
40 (b) withdrawn.
41 (b) shrink.
42 (b) awkward.
43 (c) flameproof.
44 (a) big.
45 (b) huge.
46 (a) order.
47 (b) wet.
48 (c) fed.
49 b) traditional.
50 (a) bland.

Events (64-67)

1   (b) 1963.
2   1972.
3   (c) 1948.
4   (b) 1952.
5   1963.
6   (c) 1937.
7   1944.
8   (c) 1906.
9   1929.
10 (a) 1980.
11 (c) 1903.
12 1953.
13 (a) 1982.
14 (b) 1985.
15 (c) 1949.
16 1972.
17 (c) 1964.
18 (b) 1869.
19 1970.
20 (a) 1900.
21 (c) 1924.
22 (b) 1959.
23 1961.
24 (b) 1967.
25 (c) 1974.
26 (c) 1911.
27 (a) 1912.
28 1973.
29 (a) 1955.
30 (b) 1969.
31 (b) 1940.
32 1968.
33 (c) 1948.
34 (b) 1956.
35 (a) 1960.
36 1976.
37 (b) 1960.
38 (a) 1934.
39 1933.
40 (b) 1938.
41 (a) 1975.
42 (c) 1978.
43 1980.
44 1920s.
45 1970s
46 (a) 1973.
47 (c) 1990.
48 1988.
49 (b) 1984.
50 (a) 1952.

The Arts (68-71)

1   Stan Laurel.
2   1949.
3   Ethel Merman.
4   'What's up, Doc?'
5   1931.
6   Amos 'n' Andy.
7   1967.
8   Toulouse Lautrec.
9   Tahiti.
10 *Evita.*
11 Deanna Durbin.
12 *Grand Hotel.*
13 Bette Davis.
14 Quentin Crisp.
15 Christopher Lee.
16 Robert Burns.
17 Mr Spock.
18 Dylan Thomas.
19 Bob Dylan.
20 Woodstock.
21 The violin.
22 Stradivari.
23 It is a corruption of 'jaws harp', the instrument being held between the teeth.
24 Napoleon Bonaparte.
25 Manet.
26 *The Waste Land* by T.S. Eliot.
27 Dylan Thomas.
28 Mervyn Peake.
29 *1984* by George Orwell.
30 Samuel Johnson.
31 Stephen Crane.
32 Alec Guinness.
33 *Four Weddings and a Funeral.*
34 *The Last of the Mohicans.*
35 Helena Bonham-Carter.

ANSWERS

36 Moomins.
37 Gandalf.
38 Sauron.
39 Tom Sawyer and Huckleberry Finn.
40 Brobdingnag.
41 *A Clockwork Orange*.
42 A leopard.
43 Mark Twain (according to Huck Finn).
44 *Peter Pan*.
45 Tarzan of the Apes.
46 Sweeney Todd.
47 Pippi Longstocking.
48 Agatha Christie.
49 Marie.
50 Marvin Lee Aday.

Inventions (72-75)

1 Alexander Graham Bell.
2 Television.
3 It was an early lie-detector.
4 Microsoft; Bill Gates.
5 The jukebox.
6 To raise water.
7 Charles Babbage.
8 The first safe, and reasonably fast, passenger lift.
9 It was a form of central heating.
10 The Earl of Sandwich.
11 Alexander the Great.
12 Thomas Edison.
13 The wheel.
14 The Chinese.
15 Scandinavia.
16 Wales.
17 The saddle.
18 The whip.
19 The pendulum clock.
20 The slide rule.
21 Porcelain false teeth.
22 The Spinning Jenny.
23 Copper plated with a thin layer of real silver.
24 The parachute.
25 Bifocal lenses.
26 The Montgolfiers (in 1783).
27 He invented the steel nib in 1780.
28 John McAdam.

29 The first single-purpose electronic computer.
30 Photography.
31 Singer.
32 Adolphe Sax.
33 Nitroglycerine. It was a very unstable explosive.
34 He invented the photographic negative.
35 Samuel Morse.
36 The hypodermic syringe.
37 Colour photography.
38 He invented a machine to make it.
39 Fixing the soles to the uppers of shoes.
40 It was a primitive horseshoe tied on with leather thongs.
41 Chewing gum.
42 Coca Cola.
43 Waterman invented an improved ink supply so that the pen neither dried up nor flooded.
44 The bark of the willow tree.
45 The sphygmomanometer.
46 For security reasons it was pretended that they were water-storage tanks.
47 Diabetes.
48 Toothbrush bristles.
49 The glass cats' eyes used as road markings.
50 DDT.

People (76-79)

1 1963.
2 Samuel Goldwyn.
3 Popeye.
4 Helen of Troy's.
5 Allen. Bob Dylan was born Robert Allen Zimmerman and Woody Allen was Allen Stewart Konigsberg.
6 Grigori Yefimovich Rasputin.
7 Sergeant Pepper.
8 John Wayne.
9 Mark Twain.
10 Bonnie and Clyde.
11 Mohandas Karamchand Gandhi.

12 George Washington.
13 Robinson Crusoe.
14 Athos, Porthos, Aramis, and D'Artagnan.
15 Boo Radley.
16 Martin Luther King, Jr.
17 Muhammad Ali.
18 King Harold II.
19 Stalin.
20 Captain James Cook.
21 Tarzan.
22 The FBI.
23 Guy Fawkes.
24 Marie Curie.
25 Huckleberry Finn.
26 Lyndon Baines Johnson.
27 Santa Anna.
28 The typewriter.
29 Orenthal James.
30 General de Gaulle.
31 Allan Pinkerton.
32 A short-barreled pistol that had a large bore and was small enough to be carried in a pocket.
33 He wrote *Alice in Wonderland* under the name of Lewis Carroll.
34 James Cagney.
35 Sitting Bull.
36 Blackbeard.
37 Billy the Kid.
38 The Starship Enterprise.
39 George Orwell.
40 Anne.
41 Gulliver.
42 Dr Samuel Johnson.
43 Nelson.
44 Joan of Arc.
45 Robert the Bruce.
46 Benito Mussolini.
47 Tenzing Norgay.
48 Superman.
49 Robin Hood.
50 Sir Isaac Newton.

Places (80-83)

1 Morocco.
2 Switzerland and France.
3 Tasmania.
4 Arizona.
5 A prison.
6 India.
7 Namibia.
8 Roman Catholic.
9 Hammerfest.
10 Austria.
11 Lizard Point.
12 Brooklyn.
13 Germany.
14 Istanbul.
15 Kashmir.
16 Denmark.
17 The Black Sea.
18 Table Mountain.
19 New South Wales.
20 Lithuania, Latvia, and Estonia.
21 The Pyrenees.
22 Jakarta.
23 Tierra del Fuego.
24 Fujiyama.
25 Tiber.
26 Moscow.
27 Neither – they are both on the same latitude.
28 Shanghai.
29 Majorca, Minorca, Ibiza.
30 Copenhagen.
31 Switzerland and Austria.
32 The Inner Hebrides.
33 The Bosphorus.
34 Rabat.
35 Tunisia.
36 Lake Superior.
37 Agra.
38 Quebec.
39 Wyoming.
40 Northumberland.
41 In the Alps, on the border of Italy and Switzerland.
42 Honshu.
43 Tanganyika and Zanzibar.
44 Madrid.
45 Denver.
46 The Greater Antilles.
47 Tuscany.
48 Zambia.
49 The Rhine.
50 Portugal.

Nature (84-87)

1 Bilberry.
2 Caprifoliaceae.
3 Newfoundland.
4 Panther.
5 It is a fungus with a red cap with white patches.
6 Carnivorous.
7 In water.
8 They suck the blood from other fish.
9 A crocodile.
10 Virginia creeper.
11 Captive parrots can live to more than 80 years.
12 It has a long pointed snout and often no tail.
13 No trees: only stunted shrubs, mosses, and lichens can survive.
14 Resin.
15 35.
16 The Arctic.
17 They hang upside down from branches.
18 Alpine regions.
19 A wild goat.
20 To intimidate other animals.
21 The llama.
22 A bat.
23 In his cheek pouches, which are expandable.
24 In Central and South America and South-east Asia.
25 The white rhinoceros.
26 A wild reindeer.
27 Coniferous forests.
28 A type of butterfly.
29 The iris family.
30 The condor.
31 It trips it up.
32 On a vine.
33 Mock orange.
34 A small monkey.
35 By squeezing it.
36 Marsupials.
37 In the open savanna south of the Sahara.
38 An antelope.
39 Amphibians.
40 The anopheles mosquito.
41 The grizzly bear.
42 The mandrill.
43 Australia.
44 The sturgeon.
45 Eucalyptus leaves.
46 The tsetse fly.
47 Only young ones do: the spots disappear when they get older.
48 A small short-necked giraffe, but it has zebra-like stripes on his buttocks and legs.
49 Blood.
50 A (South American) rodent.

Islands (88-91)

1   Greenland.
2   Sardinia.
3   Madagascar.
4   The Isle of Wight.
5   The Isle of Man.
6   Formosa.
7   Corfu.
8   Sicily.
9   Hainan.
10 The Malvinas.
11 The Cyclades.
12 Sri Lanka.
13 Cyprus.
14 The Bahamas.
15 Manila.
16 Coney island.
17 Christmas Island.
18 Napoleon Bonaparte.
19 The Revelation of Saint John.
20 Cuba.
21 The Channel Islands.
22 Denmark. Copenhagen.
23 Sicily.
24 Corsica.
25 The Crimea.
26 Taiwan.
27 Borneo.
28 The Andaman Islands (and Nicobar Islands).
29 The Philippines.
30 Sri Lanka.
31 Cyprus.
32 The Seychelles.
33 South America.
34 Long Island.
35 Hawaii.
36 No, not quite.
37 Papua.
38 The Sandwich Islands.
39 An archipelago.
40 The Ryukyu islands.
41 The Gulf of Alaska.
42 Bahrain.
43 The Dominican Republic.
44 Port au Prince.
45 Hispaniola.
46 Haiti and Cuba.
47 It was used as a military base.
48 No. 8.
49 Fuerteventura.
50 The USA and the UK.

People (92-95)

1   Leda.
2   Achilles.
3   Taiwan.
4   Lawrence of Arabia.
5   Lord Palmerston.
6   Commissioner Nayland Smith.
7   The marathon.
8   John Milton.
9   Holden Caulfield.
10 Count Otto von Bismarck.
11 Beria.
12 Boudicca.
13 Neptune.
14 Pontius Pilate.
15 Toulouse Lautrec.
16 Pablo Picasso.
17 A Perfect Day for Bananafish.
18 Franny.
19 Sanjay. All the others were assassinated (Mohandas and Indira by guns, Vijay by a bomb). Sanjay died in a plane crash.
20 Polyphemus.
21 Loki.
22 Sita.
23 Dr Zhivago.
24 Horsa.
25 Napier.
26 Konrad Adenauer.
27 Elhanan.
28 He was the only person known from forensic evidence whose death was caused by crucifixion.
29 He was one of the great clowns of all time.
30 Cary Grant.
31 Fred Astaire and Ginger Rogers.
32 Franco Zeffirelli.

ANSWERS

33 Alfred Nobel.

34 Harvey Firestone.

35 Don Quixote.

36 Marco Polo.

37 Captain Webb.

38 The trap failed to operate on three occasions and in the end Lee's sentence was commuted to life imprisonment.

39 Ivan Denisovitch.

40 Confucius.

41 Mahatma Gandhi.

42 Akhenaton (Amenhotep IV).

43 Lord Byron.

44 Claudius.

45 Elizabeth I of England.

46 Prince Albert.

47 In a barrel of brandy.

48 Narcissus.

49 The gorgons.

50 Charlotte Corday.

Pot Luck (96-99)

1 A googol googols.

2 They are both called Eta.

3 The Earl of Shaftesbury.

4 It lies inside an enormous extinct volcanic crater.

5 The Euphrates.

6 South-west townships.

7 *Singing in the Rain.*

8 'I'm looking for loopholes.'

9 Lord Haw Haw.

10 The Common Market.

11 President Nasser.

12 The Knesset.

13 China.

14 A protein in fibrous connective tissue.

15 'Abandon all hope, you who enter here!'

16 Lao-tzu.

17 It was the world's first printed book.

18 They were Britain's only kings since William the Conqueror not to have been crowned.

19 Gallifrey.

20 None. It is a story told of Caligula with no historical basis.

21 To make bricks without straw.

22 The mummification of corpses.

23 Seppuku.

24 The sackbut.

25 Bradford, Yorkshire.

26 Richard Dadd.

27 Evariste Galois.

28 Rastafarians.

29 No; it's a petrol bomb.

30 The tomb of Tutankhamen.

31 He set fire to the Reichstag.

32 Joseph Stalin.

33 Prosperous peasants in Czarist Russia.

34 The surrender of Robert E. Lee to Ulysses S. Grant.

35 Parsees.

36 The Spanish Armada.

37 He occupied the Falkland Islands but was heavily defeated in the ensuing war.

38 Buddha.

39 The Pillow Book of Sei Shonagon.

40 Teddy Roosevelt.

41 Peru.

42 West Germany.

43 Octavian defeated Mark Antony.

44 John Wilkes.

45 Admiral Byng's.

46 They cannot bark.

47 Sepia.

48 A traditional Japanese poem having a fixed form of 5-7-5 syllables.

49 The ludicrous misuse of a word, especially by confusion with one of a similar sound.

50 Luigi Pirandello.

Classical Music (100-103)

1 Singspiel.

2 Four.

3 Maurice Ravel.

4 Prince Igor.

5 Ludwig van Beethoven.

6 Hungarian.

7 The violin.

8 *Abdelazar* by Henry Purcell.

9 *Sheherezade* by Rimsky-Korsakov.

10 Beethoven's Ninth Symphony.

11 Nine.

12 Felix Mendelssohn-Bartholdy.

13 Oratorio.

14 Viola da gamba.

15 Johannes Brahms.

16 *Peer Gynt Suite No.1.*

17 12.

18 Ludwig von Koechel.

19 Arnold Schoenberg.

20 Bedrich Smetana.

21 The oboe family.

22 Four.

23 La Scala in Milan.

24 Joseph Haydn.

25 An interval is the simultaneous sounding of two pitches; a chord requires three or more pitches to be played at the same time.

26 Felt hammers.

27 *Carmina Burana.*

28 *Fingal's Cave.*

29 An octave.

30 The incidental music to *A Midsummer Night's Dream.*

31 Mikhail Glinka.

32 Claude Debussy.

33 The violin.

34 *Die Meistersinger von Nürnberg.*

35 The piano.

36 Aleksandr Borodin.

37 Soprano.

38 Very.

39 It has no slow movement.

40 Poland.

41 The guitar.

42 Richard Strauss.

43 Mezzo-soprano.

44 'Emperor'.

45 A stately court dance of the 17th and 18th centuries.

46 Jean Sibelius.

47 Falstaff, Otello, and Macbeth.

48 The 'Tragic'.

49 The violin.

50 A brass instrument similar in range to the tuba.

War and Battles (104-107)

1 France.

2 Austria.

3 The Austro-Russian army.

4 Lexington and Concord.

5 Soviet Union and China.

6 The English Civil War.

7 The predominance of Protestantism and Catholicism.

8 The Unionists.

9 The English Channel and the North Sea.

10 Axis.

11 Germany, Austria-Hungary, and Turkey.

12 Bull Run, on the Potomac river.

13 1917.

14 Erwin Rommel.

15 The abdication of Czar Nicholas II.

16 1954.

17 1961.

18 The Mensheviks.

19 George B. McClellan.

20 1805.

21 Louis XVI.

22 The Treaty of Paris.

23 In Yorktown.

24 Gettysburg.

25 World War I.

26 Sinai.

27 Rolling Thunder.

28 The Tet Offensive.

29 The Boer War.

30 Albania.

31 Otto von Bismarck.

32 To drive the foreign community out of China.

33 The Second Punic War.

34 Ulysses S. Grant.

35 Britain, France, and Spain.

36 The Russians.

37 The Thirty Years' War.

38 Appomattox in Virginia.

39 John II.

40 Dunkirk.

41 The Yom Kippur War.

42 The Battle of the Somme, fought in 1916.

43 Manchuria and Korea.

ANSWERS

44 In 1905. The day became known as Bloody Sunday.
45 1899-1902.
46 To drive Turkey out of Europe.
47 Carthage.
48 The Hundred Years' War.
49 Gallipoli.
50 Agincourt.

Science (108-111)

1 It has no fixed shape.
2 Oestrogen.
3 The quark.
4 An electron.
5 Neon.
6 Gunpowder.
7 Nitroglycerine.
8 Angina pectoris.
9 The solar plexus.
10 The appendix.
11 Pollen.
12 It decreases.
13 An isobar.
14 Meteorology.
15 Stratocumulus.
16 The bends.
17 A bathysphere.
18 Lignin.
19 Sclerosis.
20 Symbiosis.
21 It represents absolute zero.
22 Entropy.
23 Sir Isaac Newton.
24 Edmund Halley.
25 Calculus.
26 A gastrolith.
27 Galileo Galilei.
28 Copernicus.
29 Ptolemy.
30 William Crookes.
31 Humphrey Davy.
32 Gatling.
33 The invention of photographic processes.
34 Thomas Edison.
35 Sir Joseph Swan.
36 Samuel Colt.
37 Charles Goodyear.
38 Two men, each called William Seward Burroughs, were responsible for them.
39 The Chinese.
40 1278.
41 The thermos flask.
42 The production of explosives.
43 Proteins.
44 The sabre-toothed tiger.
45 Oxygen.
46 A deficiency in the amount of oxygen reaching body tissues.
47 An insecticide.
48 Ethyl alcohol containing no more than 1% water.
49 Heroin.
50 Ganglion.

Books (112-115)

1 Hawkeye and La Longe Carabine.
2 The Golden Ass.
3 *Watership Down*.
4 *Something Wicked This Way Comes*.
5 *Kingdom of the Wicked*.
6 Truman Capote.
7 *A Dance to the Music of Time*.
8 *The British Museum is Falling Down*.
9 *Elmer Gantry*.
10 *Les Liaisons Dangereuses*.
11 John le Carré.
12 Malcolm Bradbury wrote *Eating People is Wrong*.
13 *Brighton Rock*.
14 *The Great Gatsby*.
15 Sally Bowles.
16 Laurie Lee.
17 James Hogg.
18 Carrie.
19 Britain, Poland, and Germany.
20 Dorothy L. Sayers.
21 Ben Okri.
22 Joseph Campbell.
23 *The Black Arrow*.
24 *The Alexandria Quartet*.
25 The Indian Mutiny.
26 He was touring manager to the actor Henry Irving.
27 *A Brief History of Time*.

28 *The Black Cloud* by Fred Hoyle.
29 Milan Kundera.
30 *The Graduate* by Charles Webb.
31 *The Name of the Rose.*
32 With Love and Squalor.
33 *The Collector.*
34 *Project for a Revolution in New York* by Allain Robbe-Grillet.
35 Desmond Morris.
36 Jules Verne.
37 Spinoza.
38 Sir Thomas More.
39 *The Life of Benvenuto Cellini.*
40 Lake Woebegon.
41 *Flowers for Algernon.*
42 Eric Berne.
43 *I, Robot.*
44 Triffids.
45 *Ancient Evenings.*
46 *The King and I.*
47 *The Mandarins.*
48 *The Quiet American.*
49 Charles Darwin.
50 John Milton, *Paradise Lost.*

Popular Music and Musicals (116-119)

1 Kate Bush.
2 Ray Manzarek.
3 Wings.
4 Leonard Bernstein.
5 *Penny Lane.*
6 *Waterloo.*
7 Glenn Miller.
8 *A Night at the Opera.*
9 Louis Armstrong.
10 *The Entertainer.*
11 *Mr Tambourine Man.*
12 *Brothers in Arms.*
13 *Cats.*
14 *Holiday.*
15 Tom Jones.
16 1977.
17 *Tapestry.*
18 Andrew Lloyd Webber.
19 Annie Lennox.
20 *Mrs Robinson.*
21 Bob Dylan.
22 *What a Feeling.*
23 *Oliver!*
24 *Rumours.*
25 Gilbert and Sullivan.
26 Peter Gabriel.
27 *Love Me Do.*
28 Cole Porter.
29 *Bohemian Rhapsody.*
30 Woody Guthrie.
31 *Annie Get Your Gun.*
32 Sting.
33 Yul Brynner.
34 Buddy Holly.
35 *You Give Love a Bad Name.*
36 Shirley Bassey.
37 Reggae.
38 Mike Oldfield.
39 Harry Belafonte.
40 U2.
41 *The House of the Rising Sun.*
42 Marc Bolan.
43 *Phantom of the Opera.*
44 Edith Piaf.
45 *Your Song.*
46 Frederick Loewe.
47 Mick Jagger and David Bowie.
48 *The Rocky Horror Picture Show.*
49 Bono.
50 The Who.

Puzzle 1

A. 24. Opposite numbers are divided or added to give 24.
B. 3. Opposite numbers are multiplied or divided by 3.

Puzzle 2

34. Write the alphabet in a 3-row grid with the following values: A, J, S = 1;
B, K, T = 2; C, L, U = 3; D, M, V = 4; E, N, W = 5; F, O, X = 6; G, P, Y = 7; H, Q, Z = 8; I, R = 9. Thus, Raphael = 9 + 1 + 7 + 8 + 1 + 5 + 3 = 34.

Puzzle 3

8. In each column, top + bottom = middle, ignoring tens.

Puzzle 4

16

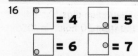

Puzzle 5

Carlos is eldest; Maccio is youngest.
(From eldest to youngest: Carlos, Juan, Za-za, Fifi, Jorjio, Maccio.)

Puzzle 6

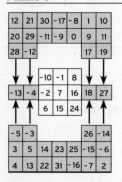

D.

Puzzle 7

30 x 15 units (the pool's area becomes 18 x 25 units, or 450 square units).

Puzzle 8

25.
Circle = 4
Triangle = 8
Diamond = 5
Square = 2
The values are added when the shapes are combined.

Puzzle 9

77 square units.

Puzzle 10

D.

Puzzle 11

E, G, G. These represent the numbers 577, which are added to the sum of the previous top and middle line, to get the bottom line.

Puzzle 12

Any number. This amazing formula will always end up with the number you first thought of, with 00 at the end.

Puzzle 13

400. The numbers are the squares of 14 to 21 inclusive.

Puzzle 14

7 people.

Puzzle 15

3. Add the rosettes and take the middle line from the top line.

ANSWERS

Puzzle 16

10 people.

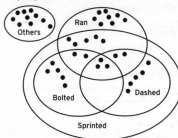

Puzzle 17

6. The right weight is nine units across to balance the left three units across. 6 x 9 (54) balances 18 x 3 (54).

Puzzle 18

Follow this route.

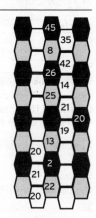

Puzzle 19

6	2	9	3	7
3	7	6	2	9
2	9	3	7	6
7	6	2	9	3
9	3	7	6	2

Puzzle 20

10 m. The ratio of the flagpole to its shadow is the same as the ratio of the measuring stick to its shadow.

Puzzle 21

D. The least number of faces touching each other gives the greatest perimeter.

Puzzle 22

1. A + B = KL, C + D = MN, and so on.

Puzzle 23

3. There are two sequences in the series:
6 x 8 = 48, and 7 x 9 = 63.

Puzzle 24

18.
Elephant = 2
Walrus = 3
Camel = 4
Pig = 5

Puzzle 25

28. Each row is a sequence of A + D = C, D + C = B and B + C = E.

Puzzle 26

Five men. Each man digs 1 hole in 5 hours, and thus 20 holes in 100 hours.

Puzzle 27

6. Add the value of the top two stars of each column to the value of the middle two stars to get the value of the bottom two stars.

Puzzle 28

200 Credits. 9 x 25 - (4 x 6.25) = 200.

Puzzle 29

21 times.

Puzzle 30

194. $(1 \times 5^3) + (2 \times 5^2) + (3 \times 5^1) + (4 \times 5^0) = 125 + 50 + 15 + 4$.

Puzzle 31

25. Star = 9, Whorl = 5, Square = 3

Puzzle 32

78. Multiply opposite numbers and add the results to get the numbers in the middle. Thus 24 + 24 + 30 = 78.

Puzzle 33

248. Long lines = 2, short lines = 1. Add the values on the right to arrive at the answer.

Puzzle 34

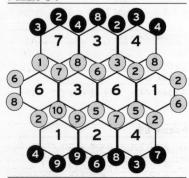

Puzzle 35

88. 88 + 880 + (4 x 8) = 1000.

Puzzle 36

27. The bottom two digits expressed as a number, subtracted from the top two digits, also expressed as a number. The difference is halved and the result is put in the middle. 78 - 24 = 54. 54 ÷ 2 = 27.

Puzzle 37

9 minutes and 9 seconds after 1.

Puzzle 38

D. The paper would reach 3,355.4432 m, which is as high as a mountain.

Puzzle 39

B. The shaded spots represent the hands of a clock. 3:00 - 9:00 = 6:00.

Puzzle 40

7. Take the middle number from the top left number. Multiply that by 2 to get the top right number. Add 5 to the top right number to get the bottom number.

Puzzle 41

42. The bottom number goes next to the top one to make a two-digit number; the left and right do the same. Then subtract the second number from the first. 96 - 54 = 42.

Puzzle 42

3		5		4		4		3		3
	90		120		64		144		54	
2		3		2		2		6		1
	48		96		16		72		36	
1		8		2		2		3		2
	160		80		20		150		30	
4		5		1		5		5		1
	180		10		40		100		15	
9		1		2		4		1		3
	27		8		32		12		81	
3		1		4		1		3		9
	24		28		84		45		135	
8		1		7		3		5		1
	144		42		63		225		25	
3		6		1		3		5		1

Puzzle 43

32.
Diamond = 7
Circle = 4
Hexagon = 13
Square = 8

Puzzle 44

38 seconds after 8.43.

Puzzle 45

7. There are 7 areas of intersection at this position.

Puzzle 46

12, 19, 26, 3, 10. The bottom line

of a magic square, in which all rows, columns, and long diagonals equal 70.

Puzzle 47

0. The top two numbers are multiplied in shapes 1, 3 and 5. The answers are put as single-digit numbers in the top triangles of shapes 2, 4 and 6. In all the shapes the top two numbers are multiplied, then halved, 3 x 0 = 0.

Puzzle 48

4. Start from the top left of the spiral and work in, successively subtracting and adding: 9 – 7 = 2, 2 + 5 = 7, etc.

Puzzle 49

103.5.

Puzzle 50

19. They denote the alphanumeric positions of numbers 1 to 6. The first letter of six is "s", the 19th letter of the alphabet.

Puzzle 51

There are 5 cards missing, leaving 47 in the deck.

Puzzle 52

22.
Rectangle = 8
Triangle = 3
Hexagon = 2

Puzzle 53

2. C = A – B, with the result reversed. 496324 – 235768 = 260556.

Puzzle 54

19. The top pair of numbers are multiplied together and added to the result of multiplying the bottom pair of numbers together: (2 x 8) + (3 x 1).

Puzzle 55

A. 54, B. 42. Opposite numbers are multiplied, divided, or added to get the numbers in the middle.

Puzzle 56

1. The number is an anagram of Mensa, with numbers substituted for the letters.

Puzzle 57

36.

912	921
x 36	x 36
5472	5526
2736	2763
32832	33156

Puzzle 58

3 units. The difference of 24 divided by 8.

Puzzle 59

6	8	0	9	4	1	6	4	1	6	2	2	2
3	4	5	6	3	4	1	2	1	9	1	8	3
6	9	1	6	1	4	4	4	3	2	7	0	8
9	2	2	8	4	6	1	5	2	9	5	5	0
0	1	6	2	1	9	3	2	0	0	0	2	5
2	8	1	3	1	2	1	5	8	5	8	7	1
9	3	9	4	5	0	4	6	3	9	5	1	2
3	1	6	1	7	6	2	1	1	3	2	6	7
7	9	2	2	8	9	6	5	6	1	2	3	1
0	2	2	3	8	4	0	4	6	1	2	8	9
8	5	4	0	4	3	2	6	1	6	1	4	2
5	2	6	1	6	0	9	3	4	1	7	2	8

Puzzle 60

96. 4^2 = 16; 16 x 6 = 96.

Puzzle 61

C - it is the same as the one above it.

Puzzle 62

24 ways. There are six alternatives with each suit at the left.

Puzzle 63

15:03

Puzzle 64

B. Each nodule is given a value, depending on its position in the grid. The values are added together.

Puzzle 65

A.
Circle = 1
Diamond = 4
Square = 3
Triangle = 2
Hexagon = 5

Puzzle 66

7162 and 3581.

Puzzle 67

2. The weight is positioned 8 units along, so it needs a weight of 2 units (8 x 2 = 16) to keep the system in balance.

Puzzle 68

A = 5. (a + b) – (d + e) = c
B = 0. (d + e) – (a + b) = c
C = 3. a + b + c – e = d
D = 2. c + d + e – a = b

ANSWERS

1. TREASURE ISLAND
GR.
1. Statue of Liberty SOL
2. Eiffel Tower ET
3. Queen Q
4. Kermit K
5. Fort Knox FK
6. Joseph J
7. Isaac Newton IN
8. Humphrey Bogart HB
9. A.D. AD
10. Prime Minister PM
11. C in Roman (Century) C

2. THE SWISS DEPOSIT CODE
1 - 5 - 6 - 2 opens the box
Letter values A=4, B=2, C=5, D=3, E=8, F=1, G=6, H=7, I=9.
DID = IIF (3x9x3) = (9x9x1) etc.

3. TAKE A SECOND LOOK
Second letters of the numbers 1 to 7. Missing letter is E.

4. TRAIN THE TRAIN DRIVER

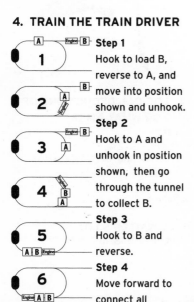

Step 1
Hook to load B, reverse to A, and move into position shown and unhook.

Step 2
Hook to A and unhook in position shown, then go through the tunnel to collect B.

Step 3
Hook to B and reverse.

Step 4
Move forward to connect all three together.

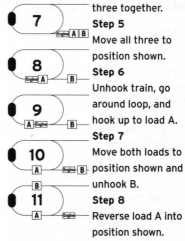

Step 5
Move all three to position shown.

Step 6
Unhook train, go around loop, and hook up to load A.

Step 7
Move both loads to position shown and unhook B.

Step 8
Reverse load A into position shown.

Step 9
Unhook train and go around the loop to position shown.

Step 10
Collect load B and reverse toward load A.

Step 11
Move load B to position shown, and return train to the original position.

5. SQUARE METRES?
The natural thing to do is to make the field square as the area of a square with the same perimeter as a rectangle will always be larger. The circle, however, always provides the greatest 2-D area.

A circle's perimeter = (pi) diameter.
if (pi)D=3000, then D=954.80 and radius (r) = 477.70.
A circle's area = (pi)r²
So the area of the circle would be 716,104.31 sq. m.
The square would be only 562,500 sq. m.

ANSWERS

6. FACT OR FICTION
February was added to the calendar by a later ruler. The early calendar only had 10 months.

7. MOVING WATER UPHILL
Put the pin through the match and pin it to the cork. Strike the match and place the cork on the water so that it floats without getting the match wet. Then put the beaker over the cork and alighted match.

The match burns the oxygen and the water will be drawn into the beaker.

8. SECRET MESSAGES
Ja COb Co = Cobalt
Alter Al = Aluminium
August's Au = Gold
Germany Ge = Germanium
UnfaIR ONe = Iron
oNE ON = Neon
Nile Ni = Nickle

9. MYSTERIES OF TIME
His 18th birthday was yesterday, New Year's Eve. He was speaking on New Year's Day, so he will have birthdays this year and next year.

10. LOGICAL THINKING WITH MATCHSTICKS

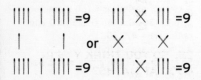

11. MORE MATCHSTICK TRICKERY!
a. Remove any two matchsticks from the same corner and use them to fill the two diametrically-opposed edge gaps. You create two small squares and one 2x2 square to replace the one you removed.
b. Remove one of the two spare matches use it to fill the edge gap next to the other spare, creating one small and one large square.

12. FRONT FOOT FORWARD
He was less than one pace from the North Pole when he planted the right foot. His left foot went over the North Pole and was therefore pointing south.

13. TRIANGLES

14. LOGICAL DEDUCTIONS OF WHO OR WHAT AM I?
1. A stallion
2. Moses
3. A calculating machine: abacus/calculator
4. A seahorse
5. Samba

15. A WAITER'S LOT
a) 14, b) 4, c) 18, d) 7, e) 8.

16. THE TRAIN DRIVER

You are the train driver, so will see whatever color eyes you have.

17. CLEANING CONFUSION

a) 15, b) 24, c) 10, d) 34, e) 73

18. A LEWIS CARROLL GEM

Just the one, but the circumstances are quite restrictive! The governor has to have a brother and a sister, and their father must also have a sister. The guest (let's call him Mr. X) must be married to the governor's aunt. Their daughter is married to the governor's brother, her cousin (which is perfectly legal, if a little risky if you want to have healthy children). Mr. X also has a brother, and this chap is the father of the spouses of both the governor and his sister. All a little cosy perhaps, but none of it illegal or immoral!

19. WORD CONNECTIONS

1. Cars:
   Lotus, Fiat, Ford, Saab and Audi.
2. Tennis players:
   Hingis, Cash, Henman and Bates.
3. Musical instruments:
   Tuba, Harp, Lyre and Drum.
4. Breeds of Dog:
   Collie, Basset, Boxer and Beagle.
5. Gems :
   Amber, Opal, Coral and Pearl.

20. CONFUSING PAPER MODEL

Cut the paper as shown along the solid lines.

Lift flap A vertically towards you, folding it at the dotted fold line. You can then then turn section B through 180° along the fold line to get the model.

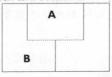

21. CONFUSING FAMILY RELATIONS

1. Alice + 3. Alice and her sister are married to brothers. The men's mother is Alice's mother's sister, who is married to Alice's father's brother. Alice's mum lives next door.
2. So are the other half.

22. LOOK FOR THE SIMPLE SOLUTION

Zero. The term (t - t) must be 0, and anything multiplied by zero is zero.

23. THE MISSISSIPPI GAMBLER

If the customer chose red, he would choose blue.
If the customer chose blue, he would choose yellow.
If the customer chose yellow, he would choose red.
He therefore should win 15 in every 27 rolls, which is 55.5%.

Red vs Blue		Blue vs Yellow	
Red	Blue	Blue	Yellow
2	3-5-7 wins	3	6-8 wins
4	5-7 wins	5	6-8 wins
9	No wins	7	8 wins

Yellow vs Red	
Yellow	Red
1	2-4-9 wins
6	9 wins
8	9 wins

24. THE FAIRGROUND GAME

a) 15
b) 3
c) 24
d) 20
e) 12

25. SO YOU THINK YOU'RE GOOD AT MATHS?

Just turn it upside down to get 81 + 19 = 100

ANSWERS

26. THE STRIPTEASE ARTIST

The manager had twisted his back. The lady was working at the bar to earn money to pay for a course as an osteopath. The manager had previously paid her for osteopathy when his back twisted before.

27. THE CAR PROBLEM

The bottom half of the wheels.

28. DOZY POLICEMEN

It was a sleeping policeman (traffic-calming road bump).

29. DECIMATED

976. The first round kills every other soldier, the second every fourth, and so on. 1000 is not a power of 2, so the last place will be as far back from 1000 as the next-highest power of two, 1024, is in front of it. So the last spot is 1000-24, or 976.

30. CHILDREN'S AGE

Children 2 - 5 - 8 - 11 - 14 - 17 - 20 - 23 - 26 : Father 48.

31. RANDOM CHANCE

None. If you get three right, the fourth will also be right.

32. THAT & THIS

'This' = x so 'That' = 8x. Then $(x+8x)/3 = x^2$, or $(9/3)x = x^2$. If $3x = x^2$, then removing an x from each side, $3 = x$ (this), and that=4.

33. THE WAREHOUSE SALE

40 - 100 - 120 (40 @ 40p = £16) + (100 @ £1 = £100) + (120 @ £1.20 = £144) Total = £260

34. THE RECTOR TOTAL

S = 0   T = 6   A = 1   O = 7
C = 2   R = 8   P = 3   L = 9
E = 4

35. COCKTAIL STICKS

1. Take alternate outside cocktail sticks to produce a separate triangle.

2. Again, remove alternate outside cocktail sticks and overlay them on the others.

3. A 3-sided pyramid.

4. Move 2 from any one of A B C or D to form squares at E and F.

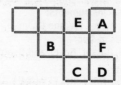

5. Move both outside cocktail sticks from B or C and complete the squares on E and F. This creates 10 squares of 1 x 1, 4 squares of 2 x 2, and one square of 3 x 3.

36. ROTATIONS
a) Number moves clockwise by original number.
b) Letter moves clockwise by one less than its alphabetical position.

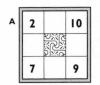

37. COMPLEX NUMBERS & LETTER GRIDS
1. 48. (A x B) - (C x D) = EF
2. M, X. 2A - B + C = D. Use alphabetical values of each letter.
3. 21. A + B + E + F = CD
4. 32. (A x B) divided by C = D

38. CHANGING WORDS
1. Seat Seam Team Tram
2. Head Heal Teal Taal Tail
3. Stone Shone Shine Thine Think Thick Trick Brick
4. White Whine Chine Chink Clink Blink Blank Black (also Clank Clack Black)
5. Here Hare Hark Hank Hunk Junk
6. Fair Fail Fall Fill Rill Rile Ride
7. Write Writs Waits Warts Wards Cards
8. Brown Brows Brews Trews Trees
9. Glass Class Clans Clank Clink Chink China
10. Green Breen Bleed Blend Bland Blank Black

39. MAGIC SQUARES

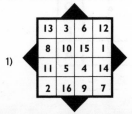
1)

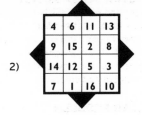
2)

40. EXTINCT? I DON'T THINK SO
Any hybrid, such as a jackass, hinney, etc.

41. THE FIRE STATION LOCATION
Halfway between A and C. This would give a maximum distance of 10 minutes to any town.

42. THE RABBIT FAMILY
8 male plus 6 female.

43. STRANGE BUT TRUE!
They suggested drawing a line on the tall man's chest level to where the short man stood. Any shot above that line was not to count.

44. THE GEARBOX
240° clockwise, and 26 times.

45. LINKS?
1. 1536. First 2 digits x second 2 digits form the next number.

2. 108. Multiply 2 outer digits of first number to form outer digits of next number. Multiply 2 inner digits of first number to form 2 inner digits of second number.

3. 27. The first 2 digits less second 2 digits form next box. Then first digit less second digit = third box.